CYNTHIA PEARSON · SAMUEL MANN · ALFREDO ZOTTI

ART THERAPY and the Creative PROCESS

A PRACTICAL APPROACH

Loving Healing Press

Ann Arbor • London • Sydney

Published by
Loving Healing Press
5145 Pontiac Trl
Ann Arbor, MI 48105

www.LHPress.com
info@LHPress.com

Tollfree (USA/CAN) 888-762-6268
FAX 734-663-6861

Library of Congress Cataloging-in-Publication Data

Names: Zotti, Alfredo, 1958- , artist, author. | Pearson, Cynthia (Cynthia
  Elaine Allen), 1965- , author. | Mann, Samuel (Samuel Augustus), author.
Title: Art therapy and the creative process : a practical approach / Cynthia
  Pearson, Samuel Mann, Alfred Zotti, and other contributors.
Description: Ann Arbor : Loving Healing Press, [2016] | Includes
  bibliographical references and index.
Identifiers: LCCN 2016013186| ISBN 9781615992966 (pbk. : alk. paper) | ISBN
  9781615992973 (hardcover : alk. paper)
Subjects: | MESH: Art Therapy | Creativity
Classification: LCC RC455.4.A77 | NLM WM 450.5.A8 | DDC 616.89/1656--dc23
LC record available at https://lccn.loc.gov/2016013186

Distributed by Ingram (USA/CAN/AU), Bertrams Books (UK/EU).

LOVING
HEALING
PRESS

Contents

Table of Figures iv

Table of Poems vi

Acknowledgements vii

Preface i

PART I - Art Works and Commentaries 3

Carol's Story by Alfredo Zotti 5

Commentary on "Grandmother" By Samuel Mann 12

Commentary on "Grandmother" a poem by Cynthia Pearson 13

Commentary on "Luciano Zotti" by Samuel Mann 15

Commentary on "Luciano Zotti" a poem by Cynthia Pearson 16

Commentary on "The Bush" by Samuel Mann 18

Commentary on "The Bush" a poem by Cynthia Pearson 19

Commentary on "Photograph 51" by Samuel Mann 21

Commentary on "Photograph 51" a poem by Cynthia Pearson 22

Commentary on "Rosalind's Eyes" by Samuel Mann 24

Commentary on "Rosalind's Eyes" a poem by Cynthia Pearson 25

Commentary on "Oriental Dream" by Samuel Mann 27

Commentary on "Oriental Dream" a poem by Cynthia Pearson 28

Commentary on "Uncle Sam" by Samuel Mann 30

Commentary on "Uncle Sam" a poem by Cynthia Pearson 31

Commentary on "September 11" by Samuel Mann 33

Commentary on "September 11" a poem by Cynthia Pearson 34

Commentary on "Violin on a Rock" by Samuel Mann 36

Commentary on "Violin on a Rock" a poem By Cynthia Pearson 37

Commentary on "The Depression Trap" by Samuel Mann 39

Commentary on "The Depression Trap" a poem by Cynthia Pearson 40

Commentary on "Colours of Emotions" by Samuel Mann 42

Commentary on "Colours of Emotions" a poem by Cynthia Pearson 43

Commentary on "The Piano Player" by Samuel Mann 45

Commentary on "The Piano Player" by Dr. Krystyna Laycraft 45

Commentary on "The Boat People" by Samuel Mann 47

Commentary on "The Boat People" a poem by Cynthia Pearson 48

Commentary on "Bits and Pieces" by Samuel Mann 50

Commentary on "Bits and Pieces" a poem by Cynthia Pearson 51

Commentary on "Yesterday, Today and Tomorrow, the Flowers" by Samuel Mann 53

Commentary on "Yesterday, Today, and Tomorrow, the Flowers" a poem by Cynthia Pearson 54

Commentary on "Venice" by Samuel Mann 56

Commentary on "Venice" a poem by Cynthia Pearson...57
Commentary on "The Shore" by Dr. Krystyna Laycraft 59

PART II- The Impact of Art Therapy **61**

Chapter 2 - Creative Writing as Therapy by Bob Rich, PhD 63

Chapter 3 - A Dream Come True! by Victor Paul Scerri...65
References...71

Chapter 4 - A Creative Journey by Krystyna C. Laycraft 73
Fascination with Nature 74
"How to Paint Infinity"..74
"The Silence" 75
Concentration on Chaos Theory..76
Interest in Individuation 77
Contemplating *I Ching* 78
Fascination with the Theory of Positive Disintegration 79
Studying the Creativity of Young People..81
Writing Books 84
Conclusion 86
References...87

Chapter 5 - "Getting the Hurt in My Head, Out": The Creative Process and Healing by
Debra Bradley 89
My Personal Story 90
Like a Part of a Gun 93
She was only Ten Years Old 96
He was Twelve Years Old...97
He was just Eleven Years Old 98
References...101

Chapter 6 - Why Music Matters: The Healing Properties of Music Therapy by Michael
Bradley...103
References...106

Chapter 7 - Cantare e Suonare è una Salvezza per l'Essere Umano By Mauro Lopizzo..........109
Singing and Playing are a Salvation for the Human Being by Mauro Lopizzo (English
Translation) 111

Chapter 8 - My Favourite Coffee Shop by Alfredo Zotti 113

Chapter 9 - My Friend Colin Sydee By Alfredo Zotti 115

Chapter 10 - Connecting with Art: My Experience with Homeless Youths by Samuel Mann
....117
References...130

Chapter 11 - Poets of the Caribbean Circle (POTCar)...131
If Only I Could Paint by Alan Pena 133
Let Me Touch You There by Alan Pena 134

Chapter 12 - Healing on the Run by Ernest Dempsey 135

Chapter 13 - Singing to Heal by Judy Wright...137

Part III - Authors, Artists, and Other Contributors **139**

Cynthia Pearson 139

Samuel Mann 141

Krystyna Laycraft 143

Dr. Bob Rich 145

Victor Paul Scerri...147

Debbie Bradley & Michael Bradley..148

Paul Corcoran 148

Alan Pena 149

Ernest Dempsey 149

Judy Wright..149

Alfredo Zotti 150

Bibliograpy 153

Index...155

Table of Figures

Fig. 1-1: Grandmother by Alfredo Zotti 11

Fig. 1-2: Luciano Zotti by Alfredo Zotti 14

Fig. 1-3: The Bush by Alfredo Zotti 17

Fig. 1-4: Photograph 51 by Alfredo Zotti 20

Fig. 1-5: Rosalind's Eyes by Alfredo Zotti 23

Fig. 1-6: Oriental Dream by Alfredo Zotti 26

Fig. 1-7: Uncle Sam by Alfredo Zotti 29

Fig. 1-8: September 11 by Alfredo Zotti 32

Fig. 1-9: Violin on a Rock by Alfredo Zotti 35

Fig. 1-10: The Depression Trap by Alfredo Zotti 38

Fig. 1-11: Colours of Emotions by Alfredo Zotti 41

Fig. 1-12: The Piano Player by Alfredo Zotti 44

Fig. 1-13: The Boat People by Alfredo Zotti 46

Fig. 1-14: Bits and Pieces by Alfredo Zotti 49

Fig. 1-15: Yesterday, Today, and Tomorrow, the Flowers h by Alfredo Zotti 52

Fig. 1-16: Venice by Alfredo Zotti 55

Fig. 1-17: The Shore by Alfredo Zotti 58

Fig. 3-1: Painting with my eyes closed -- Victor Paul Scerri 68

Fig. 3-2: The monkey painted with my eyes closed after simple meditation in 2005 while in Tokyo, ...69

Fig. 3-3: The gorilla painted with my eyes closed after simple meditation while in Tokyo, Japan. 70

Fig. 4-1: My first paintings (1994/95) 74

Fig. 4-2: Pastes of skies, (2003/2004) 75

Fig. 4-3: Acrylics of trees, (2003/2004) 75

Fig. 4-4: Paintings of bifurcations: Triptych of Kantor, Strzemiński, Dali, (2004/2005) 76

Fig. 4-5: Paintings of attractors of love, pleasure, power, and knowledge, (2004/2005) 76

Fig. 4-6: Persona, Mixed Media, (2005) 77

Fig. 4-7a: Twelve examples of collages of hexagrams: #1. Creative, #14 Inner Wealth, #16 Enthusiasm, #22 Grace, #23 Splitting Apart, #26 78

Fig. 4-7b Twelve examples of collages of hexagrams: Major Restraint, #43 Breakthrough, #34 Great Strength, #13 Fellowship, #33 Retreat, #40 Liberation, #17 Following, (2008/2009) 79

Fig. 4-8 Collages of the five levels of positive disintegration, (2012) 80

Fig. 4-9: Collages – Four Perspectives of Studying Creativity (2012) 81

Fig. 4-10 Collages representing the six participants of my study: Stephanie—The Scuba Diver, Krista Jennings—The Contortionist, Eton—The Spiritual Artist, Jade—The Art Teacher, and Alasdair MacEwan—The Young Composer (2012) 82

Fig. 4-11: Collage of Culture Perspective of Creativity, (2012) 83

Fig. 4-12: A conceptual model of the creativity of young people 84

Fig. 4-13: Krystyna Laycraft's publications (2012-2015) 85

Fig. 4-14 Illustrations for A Journey through the Lands of Feelings (2014) 86

....91

Fig. 5-1: This one represents the pain that sexual abuse causes...92

Fig. 5--2: "I painted fastasy-lands where all was pure and perfect" 94

Fig. 5-2: "I painted beautiful murals and fantasy lands where all was pure and perfect" 95

Fig. 5-3: "This is the Creeper" 96

Fig. 5-5a: Magical King of the Sea 99

Fig. 5-5b: "I feel so free..." 99

Fig. 5-5c: Black Bird 100

Fig.5-5d: "Birds are flying through the air" 100

Fig. 10-1: Hope 120

Fig. 10-2: Michael Jordan 121

Fig. 10-3: Love 122

Fig. 10-4: Hip Hop 123

Fig. 10-5 Guitar Player 124

Fig. 10-6: Picasso 125

Fig. 10-7: Horse and Man 126

Fig. 10-8: Bob Marley 127

Fig. 10-9: Lost in Thought 128

Fig. 10-10: Homeless 129

Fig. 11-1: POTcar logo 132

Fig. 14-1: Portrait of Cynthia Pearson drawn by Alfredo Zotti with white and normal pencils 139

Fig. 14-2: Drawing of Samuel Mann by Alfredo Zotti 2015 141

Fig. 14-3: Portrait by Alfredo Zotti special ink, pencils and other media, 2015 143

Fig. 14-4: Portrait of Bob Rich by Alfredo Zotti 2014. Pastels and pencils 145

Fig. 14-5: Caricature of Victor Paul Scerri, who is a wonderful friend and a sport, by Alfredo Zotti (2015) 147

Fig. 14-6: Musician, composer, and multi-talented visual artist Alfredo Zotti at the piano 150

Table of Poems

Grandmother 13

Luciano Zotti 16

The Bush 19

Photograph 51 22

Rosalind's Eyes 25

Oriental Dream 28

Uncle Sam 31

September 11 34

Violin on a Rock 37

The Depression Trap 40

Colours of Emotions 43

The Boat People 48

Bits and Pieces 51

Yesterday, Today, and Tomorrow, the Flowers 54

Venice 57

How to Paint Infinity 74

The Silence 75

I want my teddy 91

Heroes are not real 91

Like a Part of a Gun 93

You tore our hearts apart 98

If Only I Could Paint 133

Let Me Touch You There 134

Acknowledgements

While there are many people I would like to acknowledge, it would be impossible in the space of this book. This is because I do not believe in the possibility of an absolute author and, therefore, the idea of copyright as conceived in the Western World is highly problematic to say the least. Every day, we learn from the world around us, and most of what we learn comes from the minds and ideas of other people. Because of this, I would like to thank all those who have somehow contributed to my understanding of life and, in particular, my friends on Facebook, on the various websites where I help many people with mental problems, and all the people who help me every day. Thank you to everyone from the bottom of my heart and particularly to those who have helped me to create this book.

Alfredo Zotti

Preface

Many books, articles, essays, and journals have been written on Art and Creative Therapies, and while the content of the literature is often good, there are almost always complexities that obfuscate the discussions and debates.

Art and Creativity can be simple endeavours but also natural, particularly in the practical hands of artists, and we should not read too much into these human activities, but rather, practice them and be involved in the artistic creation in as many ways as possible. Indeed, today we put too much effort into writing research books and papers on creativity, rather than helping our young people be more creative in a practical fashion, which can ultimately help our social world. In many instances, our ideologies prevent the creative process and even stump it.

The most beneficial aspect of these processes is that the person creating, no matter how valuable and respectable the work of art is, will always lose him- or herself in the process, often forgetting his or her problems, commitments, and daily routine. The creator can become so involved in the process that he or she will forget daily problems. This can be extremely therapeutic and beneficial to the mind, and it is what I really value about the creative process.

But there is more to it because the artist, or the amateur artist, is often able to confront life in all of its intricate, positive, and negative elements. The creator learns to understand life and looks at it with a critical mind. This effort further fuels his or her creativity as the individual learns to evaluate life independently from ideology and from the commonsensical way of doing and thinking. Mind you, it can be a difficult process to evaluate life critically, which may be why many artists often develop mental disorders, or, alternatively, they already had mental disorders, which helped them to gravitate towards the creative arts. I feel that real artists will always suffer with some mental disorders; it is part of the creative process.

I want to leave these processes as they are without reading too much into them. I want to look at the practical aspects of creating, the ideas behind the act of creation. Creativity is what humans do; we create ideas in our mind, ideas that are then translated into artistic works, practical ways of doing things, and even daily strategies. Creativity is not confined to visual art, or music or poetry, or any other artistic activity alone, but it can also be found in the form of a unique way to type at the computer, or a creative strategy at work or at home. In this book, however, the focus is on creative writing, visual art, and poetry.

In the first part of this book, I feature photos of my paintings and drawings done with different media. These are complemented by the beautiful poems of Cynthia Pearson and the very analytical mind of Samuel Mann, a very talented artist and writer. With the help of these wonderful people, I have been able to capture something about the artistic and creative process, and that is to reveal the possible mental activities that often go with the work of art, either during conception, before or after, when critics and commentators look at the work. Like everything else, what we see is both unique and universal. There is never one way to look at a work of art. The work is most often interpreted by the viewer just as each of us interprets life. Yet all of these interpretations are valuable and correct because they generate ideas in the viewer, creative ideas that come to life.

In the second part of this book, I will include many articles by friends, academics, and professional therapists who will help to shed more light on the Artistic and Creative Therapeutic Processes. There will never be a final and complete understanding of what Art Therapy and Creativity are, but this book aims to invite the reader into the creative world of the human mind. It is just a peek, just a quick look at what remains a mystery in terms of explaining it. No matter how much writers attempt to capture, define, and pin down these creative processes, we can never fully understand their complexities. But we can be part of the activities that make up these processes. In other words, it is much easier to engage in the process than to try to explain it. There is no doubt that certain aspects will never be fully understood.

Alfredo Zotti

PART I -
Art Works and Commentaries

Carol's Story
by Alfredo Zotti

During the 1930s and the Great Depression, most of the industrialized countries found themselves in a financial crisis caused by the collapse of the world market. Carol, then a young woman, decided to settle and work as a waitress in Sydney, Australia. She was born in Tasmania and had lived there all of her life before coming to Sydney. Given that it was still possible for some people to afford a cup of tea and some cake, she managed to find a little part-time job in a tea cake shop.

One evening as Carol was going home, she encountered the unusual sight of a well-dressed man sleeping on a park bench with his face covered by an old newspaper. As she quickly walked by to pass unnoticed, the man suddenly woke up and caused her to trip, hurting her leg in the process. She was terrified, but the man understood and said, with a strong European accent, "No fear, no fear, Miss. I will not hurt you. Let me help you up."

Carol felt a sense of relief. With the help of the nice man, she got up and they both headed towards the park bench where they sat together. At first, there was silence as Carol came to terms with her excruciating pain. Soon she asked the man, "Where are you from?"

"I come from Yugoslavia," the man said. Yugoslavia is today known as Serbia, but back in those days, it was still Yugoslavia. "They promised me lots of work, and that is why I decided to come here, but now I cannot find any work," he continued. "I wait each morning, in line, hoping for some work down at the construction sites, but I have to be lucky to get some part-time work, and I cannot afford a place, so I sleep in the streets and use the public toilets to wash."

Carol looked at him and noticed his kind eyes. She said, "It looks like you are in luck for tonight. You will have to help me home. You can stay for the night. I will let you sleep on the lounge."

The days went by fast. Carol came to trust Paul (this was the name of the nice Yugoslavian man) so much so that she asked him to stay with her for a while till he had a roof over his head. She cared for him and did not want him to sleep out in the rough.

Paul was not your average man. He was extremely caring and gentle, and he respected Carol very much. He treated her like a real person, not like how some men treat women as inferior sexual objects. He was a real friend to Carol and really appreciated her kindness and desire to help him.

Paul would work occasionally part-time because he was a good worker. But the competition for work was fierce during the depression because many people were willing to work hard. Carol and Paul had a friendly relationship. They had had no sex yet, but they cared for each other. The ingredients for a great relationship were certainly there. Unfortunately for Carol, as soon as Paul got some money together, he went to visit some people he knew to borrow enough money to buy some land that was suitable for a tomato farm. He always wanted to grow tomatoes and make a living as a tomato farmer.

He borrowed thirty pounds (which would be the equivalent of about 12,000 dollars today) and went up to a place called Kariong, situated on the Central Coast of New South Wales, to buy a piece of land. The first thing he did was to build his house while he slept in a tent that he had made with recycled materials, and he worked with the local council, part-time, to earn a living. The land was quite big, forty acres, ideal for growing tomatoes, or so he thought.

Carol and Paul kept seeing each other on weekends. Paul would catch the train to Sydney, which was a couple of hours away from Kariong. Sometimes, Carol would visit Paul and sleep in the tent.

By now, their relationship was complete and Carol and Paul were thinking about their future. They planned to get married.

Paul learned that Carol had two sons, Cyril, who was twenty-four, and John, age twenty-six, who lived independently at the time. Carol had been married twice, but she had never known a man like Paul—a real equal partner who treated her like a real person.

Paul continued to work with the council, and this was just as well because as soon as he built the house and started to plant the tomatoes, he discovered that the land flooded quite frequently. Twice he lost his tomato crop. Realizing that the tomato farm was not possible, Paul continued to work until he got a permanent job with the local council. It was not easy to work in those days because migrants were discriminated against in all sorts of ways. But Paul was such a good worker that he soon became the gang leader and was in charge of nine men who worked with him to build roads and he took care of the workers.

Carol continued to work as a waitress and visit Paul every weekend. Eventually, Paul built a house, and Carol and Paul decided to get married. They got married in 1937 and continued to struggle until the end of the depression, two years later, in 1939. The years went on into the 1950s. Paul continued to work for the council while Carol travelled to Sydney to work in a coffee shop. Life was busy and the days went by fast. But something terrible was about to happen to Carol and, fortunately, Paul was there to ensure that she survived the ordeal.

Of course, this story is mostly true, but there are always parts that contain some fiction because it is impossible to tell an accurate story of past events. Carol and Paul had survived the Great Depression and the Second World War, and although news of terrible things came to them via the old valve radio and newspapers, Kariong was a reasonably quiet place. Most of the inhabitants were almost self-sufficient.

Paul had been able to find bore water (water that is stored naturally underground). Kariong was famous for it. With that endless supply of water located on his land only twenty meters away from the house, Paul was able to grow all sorts of vegetables. This time he made sure to plant his crops on a hill so the floods would not kill the plants. He had been able to grow potatoes, zucchini, watermelons, strawberries, carrots, celery, beans, and many other vegetables. Near the house there were fruit trees. This abundance was incredible and the soil very fertile. He used what vegetables he could, and the rest he would sell with Carol at the local markets, on a Sunday, or give some away to friends and visitors. And, of course, there were chickens for eggs. It was a self-sufficient little farm that Paul had established on his property. In addition, Paul loved dogs and he had a couple of miniature fox terriers running around the land, for alarm and protection.

Kariong was, and is, a beautiful place. The air was pure up to the 1980s when I, the writer of this story, and my wife, went to live with Carol in Kariong. By then, Paul had died and Carol was left alone with her memories. But this is for later.

The name Kariong, once believed to mean "Meeting Place," and after, "Place of the Cold Winds," was just a typographical error from the old script "Karrong." The second "r" was mistaken for an "i," giving the name Kariong. The first British settler was W.H. Parry, who arrived in 1901. And the name Kariong was not given until 1947. Prior to that, Paul had called the land Penang Mountain

Mount Penang training mountain opened in 1911 and was a kind of correction and training centre for young boys who had lost their way or young convicts who arrived from England. Paul had met Bill Dibden, who worked as an officer at the centre where he took care of the young boys and was like a father figure to them. Bill was a wonderful man who cared for the youths, all of whom he helped to became good men and hard workers with family. I met Bill in the late '80s, but for now, let's go on with the description of Kariong.

Kariong still has some of the most unique plants and flowers. The Brisbane National Park was only a few meters away from Paul's House. I remember when I lived there for a while I used to go into the National Park and either take photos of that beautiful natural and wild place or just sit there among the ancient aboriginal drawings. I would often spot a wallaby (small kangaroo), and sometimes there were other little animals that were not afraid of me but simply minded their own business. Of course, there were snakes (the red belly snake) and spiders (funnel web spiders), but they did not bother me if I left them alone. And also there were plenty of birds. Kookaburras, magpies, and craws were plentiful, but also the other rare smaller birds. I always had my way of getting on with all sorts of animals.

Kariong was a beautiful place where natural resources were abundant. For example, Kariong is the original place where the original Waratah flower comes from; it then spread to other areas of New South Wales. Carol and Paul lived in this beautiful area, a paradise that had plenty of natural resources to offer. Every day, they thanked God for having made it possible for them to live in such a paradise and to have each other. And, of course, they went to church every Sunday before going to the markets.

But their beautiful, clean, and simple life was about to be disrupted by a terrible event that affected Carol for the rest of her life. It was near Christmas and the afternoon was very hot. The beautiful Christmas bells had grown all along Paul's road. It was a natural spectacle of red and yellow colours. The road was quite wide and right in the middle of a dense bushy area. The people of Kariong knew no danger, and even women could freely walk in the middle of the night, knowing they were very safe. Everyone knew one another. There were only a few inhabitants in Kariong. It was more like a village where people had good old values and respect for each other.

That afternoon, Carol decided to go to the Langfords, the post office opposite the community hall, which was only a few meters up the main road, just off of Paul's road. Paul reminded Carol to get a few envelopes because he had to write to his family in Yugoslavia. Given that the temperature was rising, he decided to water his vegetables and kept on working in the garden, forgetting that time was passing quickly. It was nearly dark. There was always something to do. When he finally decided to go back inside, he found Carol sitting silently at the table with a ghostly face and a telegram hanging from her lifeless hand that had dropped to the left side of her body.

"What's the matter, Carol? Are you ok?" Paul asked with a serious expression.

"Read the telegram, Paul. I can't speak," said Carol.

Paul picked up the telegram from Carol's hand and had a quick look.

"It's from your son, John."

He kept on reading the telegram.

> Dear mum,
>
> I am writing this letter and find that tears are running down my face. I have developed lung cancer shortly after Kathleen died with an aneurysm, and I married again, but I wish I hadn't. My second wife is now looking after the kids, but I know that she is a gambler, an alcoholic, and possibly takes drugs, and is not feeding the kids. She mistreats the kids, I was told by Nevil (Cheryl's stepbrother), and I fear for Cheryl, who is only four years old. I was told that the woman is not changing Cheryl's nappies and she is not feeding her. I fear that she may die. Please send someone to check up before it is too late. I am in Brisbane hospital (up in Queensland), and I have been here for three weeks now. Doctors said that they cannot do anything for me and that I will die soon.

By now, tears had begun to run down Paul's face. He remembered John, the young man who had fought in the war and had a heart of gold. He had helped him to build the road that made life easy for the seven neighbouring houses there. They had built a dirt road with their bare hands and called it Paul's road. In those days, Kariong had just one main road, which today is best known as Woy Woy road.

Carol looked at Paul with tenderness and with a very soft voice said:

"I am going to Queensland to see John. I will ring you as soon as I get there. Paul, you look after things around here. I will be back with Cheryl. I am going straight to the police to make sure that they give me custody of Cheryl. And I will visit John at the hospital to put his mind at rest."

When Carol arrived in Brisbane, she headed straight to the police station. After the police read John's telegram about the way in which his second wife had treated little Cheryl, the police decided to go with Carol to the house to see the condition in which Cheryl was living. When they arrived, they found a poor little girl in a broken baby cot barely breathing, soaked in urine, and almost blue in the face. Only Cheryl's stepbrother and her stepsister were with Cheryl and taking care of her. The stepmother had gone to gamble down at the club. The police found her and charged her. She was to appear in court on a serious charge of neglect and abuse with a possible jail sentence if she did not pay a substantial fine. Young Cheryl was taken to the hospital, the same hospital where John was dying of lung cancer. Carol accompanied her in the ambulance.

Carol stayed at the hospital for a couple of days, thanks to the kindness of the doctors and nurses. She was fortunate to talk to John. In his last hour, John told Carol how much he wanted to eat some of Paul's pasta, but, of course, he could not eat; and how happy he was that Cheryl was being looked after. Finally, his little girl was safe. John died in peace the next day. Carol had promised him that thereafter, Cheryl would be her daughter and she would take good care of her. For a moment, she stopped to think how some people ruined their children's lives without being fully aware of what they were doing. If they were truly aware, they could not have lived with themselves. So many children were traumatized because of parental failures—because of alcohol, gambling, and drugs.

It was sunny that day when Carol and Cheryl headed to the airport. Cheryl was only four years old, but she had been so traumatized that she was very shy and quiet. She made no sound, but Carol could sense that the little girl had been severely affected by the terrible ordeal of having lost her parents at such a young age. Her only possessions were a broken doll and a little bag to place her doll in. She had nothing else. Cheryl is my wife today. I have read many similar stories from traumatized people, stories of how children are traumatized by their parents.

When Carol returned home from the long train trip, she made Cheryl a nice warm pumpkin soup, all mushed up, and showed her the way to her room, an extension that Paul had built while Carol was up in Brisbane to get Cheryl and say goodbye to her dying son. Paul was a very resourceful man, an old-fashioned man who could do almost anything. When he returned from work, he found Cheryl sleeping. She was exhausted, but at least she was well taken care of now, with food in her little stomach and some love.

"How is Cheryl?" He said.

"She hasn't said a word since I got her," Carol replied. "I'm not sure if she will ever speak or make any noises with her vocal chords."

"We'll see," said Paul.

The next morning, Paul came in with a miniature foxy under his arm and gave it to Cheryl after she had breakfast. It was then that Cheryl made some noises with her voice. And when Paul told her that this was Trixie, she tried to repeat the name, which signalled that there was nothing wrong with Cheryl's voice.

Carol was nearing middle age and so was Paul, and the last thing they wanted was to raise more children. But now they had Cheryl to look after, so there was no way out. Carol loved little Cheryl. She was the only thing that her son had left her. She was precious and beautiful, and as the years went on, she grew into a beautiful and charming young woman.

When Cheryl got her diploma in shorthand writing and bookkeeping, she left Carol and Paul to work in a more suitable area. There was no work in Kariong for a secretary. It was just a small village in those days. Cheryl soon found out how terrible the world was: she married an alcoholic man from New Zealand who was abusive and violent. He forced her to run away from him and find refuge back in Kariong with Grandmother Carol and Grandfather Paul. She was a smart woman, Cheryl, because many women remain in abusive relationships, especially if there are children involved. As soon as Cheryl became emotionally strong again, she went away to work in a government job and then, afterwards, as a manageress for a clothing company.

Life in Kariong was the same as it had always been, except that Paul and Carol where getting old. Paul developed Alzheimer's and Carol had her hands full looking after him. Paul had retired from the council job, as the gang leader, a few years back. The men liked him so much that they all gave him presents and bought him a wallet, which they filled with money they donated. Paul was the best boss they had ever had. He was not only their boss, but he had been a father to them, always showing great respect for the workers and using his good values to help people. He was a man of principle, a man of his word like very few are today. After his retirement, Paul dedicated himself to growing vegetables, looking after his trees and his dogs, and taking care of Carol, of course. Life was good. It was clean and honest. The neighbours were all good hardworking people, and most had their own veggie gardens. Those who did not have a garden got free veggies from their neighbours, and believe me, there was more than enough to feed an entire small village or an army.

The years went on, and life for Cheryl changed for the better when she met me. We were both working in Kings Cross, I as a pianist and she as a drink manager at the Manzil room, a popular nightclub where many famous entertainers and musicians performed. Both before and after work, Cheryl used to come by to have a drink where I played the piano and to listen to my music. It was there that we met and developed a friendship and then a relationship. Eventually, we got married, and when we both lost our jobs, for various reasons, we decided to go visit with Grandmother Carol, who was kind enough to let us stay at her place for a while. In those days, people did not rely on welfare, and Cheryl and I certainly didn't. We had some money set aside, money I had saved while I continued to do some part-time work as a musician at wedding receptions. The funny thing is that two nights in at this Italian reception centre, I had earned more than I had playing six days as a pianist.

I really enjoyed my stay at Kariong. You could smell the pure fresh air. It is an experience that is hard to describe. That fresh air was a sign that the place was not polluted by progress. One could hear the bird calls, and it was clear to me that I had fallen in love with that place.

Cheryl introduced me to all of the neighbours and friends. One particular neighbour, Mrs Dibden, was her favourite. Cheryl often told me how Mrs Dibden was like a mum to her. And Cheryl loved to spend time with Mrs Dibden; she would do her hair and take care of her hands and nails and have long conversations over many cups of tea. I had become friends with Mrs Dibden's husband, Bill, who worked for many years at the correction centre for young people at Mount Penang in Kariong. He was a very nice man with strong values. He had helped many of the young people, who were orphans and had lost their way, to get back on their feet, learn a craft, and prepare for life. Bill was also a handyman and what caught my attention, back in those days, was how the men knew how to do most things like building houses, building furniture, and doing most things that many men of today would not know how to do. We seem to have lost a lot of practical knowledge along the way. Whenever something goes wrong, now we need to call the tradesman. But in those days, people were self-sufficient and relied on their own skills. This was wonderful, I thought. Women were the same. They could do most things around the house. People were self-sufficient in more ways than one.

We spent many nights at the Dibdens' with Grandmother, often having good discussions about life over nice cups of tea. Mrs Dibden was an artist and she liked to paint with oil colours. This was something that we had in common since I was also a young artist.

The life in Kariong was simple, but it was my kind of life. One day, I decided to inspect Paul's garden where he grew his vegetables, which was a fair distance from the house, right in the bushy area of the land. Paul had been dead for a few years now, but his work could still be seen in every corner of his land and his house. There I found the bore water, and I could see how big the garden was. Paul must have worked really hard there, and I could imagine all the beautiful vegetables full of flavour and colour that must have grown there. There must have been enough veggies to feed the population of Kariong and still have some left over. As I returned to the house, I hear the old valve radio announce the introduction of a new tax, a land tax.

It was the early '80s and Bob Hawke was the Prime Minister of Australia then. For some strange reason, the Labour Government came up with a tax on the land that was implemented with devastating effects on the people. All the people of Kariong were hit with this tax that they could not afford. This was all orchestrated to force the people to sell their land to the big developers. Carol, who had been a strong Labour voter, felt really let down. For a while, her son, Cyril, helped her to pay the tax until Landcom was ready to buy most of the properties. During this period, I often caught Carol thinking sadly, just as I depicted in the portrait. The land was not just a material possession for these people, the land was a symbol of who they were—hardworking people who had worked on the land most of their lives. Kariong was about to change, but fortunately for Carol, she did not see the change because she died before Kariong was transformed beyond recognition. Her son, Cyril, got possession of her house and sold the land to Landcom, a big developer that had bought most of the land of Kariong. Being a gambler, he lost most of the money, though he left a little to his relatives, except Cheryl.

Cheryl and I remained on the Central Coast where we have lived since the late '80s. We have seen Kariong become a land full of houses with inadequate resources for its inhabitants. If I drive around Kariong now, the only things that have not changed much are the Community Hall on Woy Woy Road, which stands there as a reminder to me of what the place was once, and the Brisbane National Park. The rest of Kariong is a jungle of houses, one next to the other, where people don't even know each other's names.

All of the values that were part of the moral fabric of the people of Kariong have now gone. The progress has finally taken over, wiping out the old way of life. No more vegetable gardens, no more bush-walks, no more solidarity among the people. This is a different life, the modern life. Now I understand Carol's concern, a concern that I had captured while drawing her face. Progress had not just changed the landscape, but the very nature of human beings. We have become alienated from the land, unable to grow our vegetables, unable to do most of the things the real Australian people used to do. Kariong was a real Australian place where real Australians lived, people with high moral standards, with good hearts, who cared about their community. The community spirit is almost gone. Today, I try to keep it alive. I do volunteer work because the people of Kariong taught me the importance of working for one's community, the importance of moral values and respect. I wish more people understood this.

Fig. 1-1: Grandmother by Alfredo Zotti

Commentary on "Grandmother"
By Samuel Mann

"Grandmother" is a very deeply touching moment for the artist. Not only does it brings back cherished memories of someone whose biographical history is intimately tied up with the Kariong locality in New South Wales, Australia, but it reminds the artist of something much more profound and universally troubling. As he describes it in his own words, Grandmother's portrait reflects a disturbing "concern about where the world is heading." Being a portrait artist myself, I can quickly relate to the rough and seemingly free-flowing lines that intertwine and, almost web-like, weave themselves into an image that is brutally frank to the point.

The thick round impenetrable lens, shielding downward-looking and thoughtful eyes and firmly resting on a semi-hawkish nose, attests to the solid and informed judgement of the shrewd observer of the world. The encyclopaedic lines of the forehead evidence a vast understanding of events that have transpired and are still transpiring while tightly squeezed lips buttressed by a steep, elongated chin reinforce the sturdy character of the subject. Added to all of this is the rocky-shaped and textured hairstyle, tailoring down to an ear that can be easily compared to the entrance of a cave.

One of the fascinating things about sketching is the speed and economic use of lines and shading to create an impression of wholeness. "Grandmother," with its own story and interpretation of where we are poised today as agents of humanity, is, in my opinion, a perfect execution of this art.

Commentary on "Grandmother"
a poem by Cynthia Pearson

I remember grandmother,
Her story out of Kariong cries,
A memory I'll not forget,
Strong and poised
Old and wise.
Now in portrait,
Sketched in black and white,
The bold lines capture her life,
Reaping a legacy of kindness
For sowing seeds of goodness.

I remember grandmother,
Her story out of Kariong cries,
Deep lines of concern etched
On furrowed face, contemplating,
I heard her softly breathed sighs.
Sometimes weeping,
Tears hidden behind bespectacled eyes,
She longed for a better world,
A mission that began with Paul,
Their rich life together, a testament to us all.

Fig. 1-2: Luciano Zotti by Alfredo Zotti

Commentary on "Luciano Zotti"
by Samuel Mann

This painting of the artist's father (Fig. 1-2) tells us a lot about the subject and his relationship with the artist. The smooth rolling landscape of trees and ochre-coloured turf portray a quiet and harmonious character. Together, with the bird and the river, we can suspiciously hazard that there is something musical about the individual who was, in fact, a musician. There are two perspectives shown in the painting: one is the bigger picture we see when we step back, and the other, the narrow picture when we are close up. This might perhaps be suggestive of the artist's relationship with his father, knowing him personally, which helps to explain the slightly obscured image in a compressed form, as opposed to the man and how he was actually perceived in public.

The face is either professorial-looking or that of a maestro, and not without some visible resemblance to the artist. It is interesting to note that the subject, seemingly a cut-out from another picture with a halo-like allusion of reverence behind his head, is tinted in purple, a symbolic colour of many things such as royalty, nobility, creativity, wisdom, dignity, grandeur, devotion, peace, pride, independence, and even mystery.

Commentary on "Luciano Zotti"
a poem by Cynthia Pearson

To lush, green rolling plains,
Above the mountains and down
The streams, death called him away.
Gentle with droopy eyes,
And from his soul poured
Songs of a true composer,
Wailing sounds swelling
From the orchestra....

Whisked away from the nightmares
That haunted his nights,
And banishing the pain by day,
Death took my father away.
No longer driven to imbibe,
For his inner parts did burn,
Rendering him to ash in an urn.

But I can hear his enchanting tune
In my head as I try to fall asleep,
Hauntingly keeping me up till dawn.
When the daylight breaks through
My spirit moves with the chirps,
Reminding me of my father still,
From a bird conducting his song
On my windowsill.

Fig. 1-3: The Bush by Alfredo Zotti

Commentary on "The Bush"
by Samuel Mann

Three things stand out prominently in this painting (Fig. 1-3). First of all, the luminescence of the light in the distance is instantaneously striking, while at the same time smoothly contrasting with the dark green foliage in the foreground. The shadows seem to be telling us it could be either morning or late afternoon. Aside from how skilfully the artist manages to capture the brightness of the sunlight, the second thing one admires about this piece of work is the white tree trunks, almost like birch trees, but without the characteristic spots. Since I grew up in the Caribbean, they bring back memories of cricket bats, which we used to think were made from such trees. With their effeminate purity and softness, the trees are in a lovable way, without doubt, the most attractive feature of the painting. My third observation is how the artist succeeds in effortlessly blending two colours, white and green, to reproduce an image of tranquillity, idyllic enough for the viewer to be drawn into it and be hypnotized.

Commentary on "The Bush"
a poem by Cynthia Pearson

In the forest glade among Australian Gum trees,
Where the wind like wisps blew over me,
It whispered great mysteries in my ear,
Its breath floating by, fresh like mint,
Uttering words I knew were heaven sent:

This place here brings you salubrious care.
The sun rising softly,
Its rays peeping shyly through the leaves,
For the clouds above rest on celestial sleeves.
On meadows green falls the sprinkling dew,
Fresh! On fruit and vegetable gardens too.

Here you will live and find shelter,
Lovingly embraced by the arms of nature.
Over there, flitting birds sweetly sing,
Careful of bees they know how to sting.
Watch milking cows or fowls pecking on seeds,
Take a stroll, walk where your shadow leads.

The whispering got quiet, then swiftly departed,
I smiled, curled up my toes, finally contented.
Taking in the awesome mysteries of the hush,
I welcome perfect bliss in this bucolic bush!

Fig. 1-4: Photograph 51 by Alfredo Zotti

Commentary on "Photograph 51"
by Samuel Mann

"Photograph 51" (Fig. 1-4) appears to be different from the other therapeutic works of the artist. The story behind it is the failure of the male-dominated society to acknowledge the female input into the discovery of the DNA structure by the British chemist and crystallographer, Rosalind Franklin. When I first looked at this painting, I was searching for the connection with DNA, but except for the two strands hanging from the top like ornamental decorations, the only semblance depicting the historical significance of this discovery to mankind, it does not really speak to the glory of the subject behind the painting. Instead, what I saw, and only kept seeing, were the distorted faces and profiles of sad-looking men and women, some with their heads down and others with their eyes turned away in shame. In other words, the painting, with its thematic blue tone and unhappy figures, is a reflection of the artist's own justifiable disappointment and suggestive embarrassment of humanity towards the inequitable disregard for the exemplary role of women in our society. I am reminded in a vague way of the famous scream painting by the Norwegian expressionist painter, Edvard Munch, but in this instance, the scream is a painfully silent one, originating from the heart.

Commentary on "Photograph 51"
a poem by Cynthia Pearson

Beautiful coded genes
Scream through
My crystallographic portrait,
Hidden from me in X-ray blues.
Single and complex crystals,
The solution to the riddle eludes,
Buried in my photo image.
Crystal clear to peeking eyes,
They discovered my double helix,
Twirling from my frustrated grasp.
Snatching away the prize
With masculine hands,
They overlooked me
In that beautiful photo finish.

Fig. 1-5: Rosalind's Eyes by Alfredo Zotti

Commentary on "Rosalind's Eyes"
by Samuel Mann

"Rosalind's Eyes" (Fig. 1-5) is a side profile of the brilliant British chemist and crystallographer whose crucial contribution to understanding the DNA structure was sadly relegated to a mere footnote when the Nobel Prize in Medicine for the same discovery was awarded to three male molecular biologists. This is a second tribute by Mr. Zotti to Dr. Rosalind Franklin, the other being "Photograph 51." Unlike the latter piece, which is more holistic in its interpretation, "Rosalind's Eyes" is more focused on the subject character.

At first glance, without being aware of the history and background of this drawing, to the untrained eye it would seem like an Elvis Presley portrait with the thick sideburns and famous white top he wore in one of his later stage appearances. On the contrary, it is not the actual Rosalind but the Australian actress, Nicole Kidman, who played the role of Rosalind in a theatre production. Mr. Zotti's own account of how the work was transformed with his computer from the original coloured drawing to its black and white format somehow implicitly reminds one of the endlessly long hours spent by Dr. Franklin studying pictures of DNA under a microscope.

The final product, in fact, bears some similarities to "Photograph 51," which was taken by the doctor and contained key information about the structure of the DNA. Just like an X-Ray photo, it is black and white with some parts, the hair in particular, appearing to be a little bit fuzzy, while other areas are whitish-looking and slightly discoloured. The eye is of notable significance in the drawing since several others are subtly depicted on the shirt to reveal how much the subject is now revered in history as a female scientist. It is obvious from her raised eyebrow and suggestive pout that Rosalind is not quite the happy, normal individual, having been a single woman for the duration of her life and passionately preoccupied with her work.

Commentary on "Rosalind's Eyes"
a poem by Cynthia Pearson

What do your eyes see, Rosalind?
What do your eyes see?
They are questioning, searching,
To find answers to life,
Aren't they, Rosalind? Aren't they?

What do your eyes observe, Rosalind?
What do they observe?
Those sharp, intelligent eyes,
Are bright, on the brink of discovery,
Aren't they, Rosalind? Aren't they?

What do your eyes sense, Rosalind?
What do they sense?
Those crystalline eyes sense that there
Is something more about man's DNA,
But it eludes you, Rosalind. It eludes you.

What do your eyes know, Rosalind?
What do your eyes know?
They know that in the land of the living
There will be no recognition till death, Rosalind,
That's what your eyes know.

Fig. 1-6: Oriental Dream by Alfredo Zotti

Commentary on "Oriental Dream"
by Samuel Mann

Understanding and appreciating a painting can invoke several factors. Most people connect instantly with the face value or associated effect it has on them, but having a good sense of aesthetics, and some ideas about art and the background of the painting and artist, amplifies that understanding and appreciation to a much deeper level. There are many things about this piece of work (Fig. 1-6) that I recognize. First, the frame is quite interesting in its natural form and, perhaps noticeably, says something about the artist and the painting.

Secondly, the musical notations in the painting are a calligraphic technique that I discovered many young artists use in their graffiti posters. I had a particular experience of one young artist using calligraphy and sacred geometry to convey the spiritual message in his work. This painting is not dissimilar in its therapeutic approach.

Thirdly, I like the idea of the musical notes, especially because I like to think of myself as an experientialist artist who believes that art and poetry should be integrated or packaged in such a way as to communicate not only the visual, but the process as well, to the viewer. Here, it is more symbolic than hearing the actual music to connect emotionally with the painting.

Fourthly, the quarterly-shaped moons and the stars are randomly and seemingly juxtaposed to create an oriental pattern. Hence, the title of the work.

Fifthly, the idea of using a mirror base to reflect the stars is quite innovative rather than using glitters. There is a snake-like shape in the middle that baffles me still and leaves one thinking. I suppose this is part of the intended meditation, which reminds me of the Zen riddle, "What is the sound of one hand clapping?".

Finally, the colours are not surprisingly chosen to project a healing atmosphere. It is typical of the ambience one feels in a gallery or art room. In one of my own experiences, I was amazed to witness a young girl with schizophrenia coming to sit down in an art room for a few minutes just to feel the calm and positive air of the atmosphere. She didn't need to say anything or be spoken to.

Commentary on "Oriental Dream"
a poem by Cynthia Pearson

Darkness covered my insides
With its thickness.
Pushing back the heavy shadows,
The light battles on my behalf,
Penetrating deep for its triumph.
As I embrace its warmth
And shun the familiar gloom,
Happy sparkles reflect
On my face like glittering glass
In an Oriental Dream.
Then hope beckons me to weave
Within the glow of life, joining the sunlight,
Knitting with the moon and stars,
To dance their celestial tune.
Leaping with healing joy,
My body and soul sing
And the colourful rays of light

Fig. 1-7: Uncle Sam by Alfredo Zotti

Commentary on "Uncle Sam"
by Samuel Mann

"Uncle Sam" (Fig. 1-7) represents the typical greedy old man with bright protrusive eyes focused only on getting more of what he desires. The puffiness of the beard in a way reminds us of Santa Claus because that is the image of how he wants us to see him, the benevolent savoir and sharer of happiness. Note the artist's conspicuous use of the monetary green colour, which also depicts jealousy and is another characteristic of Uncle Sam's greediness. Though old, meaning that he is wise and experienced, Uncle Sam is wearing blue jeans, which identifies him with youth and Western culture. He is portrayed as being solidly strong with an upright posture and chest pushed outward, symbolizing the power of capitalism. The swarthy complexion, hands resting at the side, and pastel effect seem to project a certain dull, but gloomy and overarching sadness.

Commentary on "Uncle Sam"
a poem by Cynthia Pearson

You stare far away into space
With your lupine face,
Protruding beady eyes,
Your beard heavy in disguise,
You sit there, your eyes shifting.
Thinking how you can kill this cow,
Curdling my milk into cash
You left nothing for my fledging calf.
You plan and scheme; I was the fool;
You used me like a tool,
Pondering what you can get.
Not seeing your arrogance and greed
You took it all; eventually you win,
Sucking me dry like a seed,
And even when I tried to numb my pain,
You took that away, stealing my last bottle of gin.

Fig. 1-8: September 11 by Alfredo Zotti

Commentary on "September 11"
by Samuel Mann

"September 11" (Fig. 1-8) is the artist's attempt to capture the devastation and shock of one of the most heinous acts in history. It is stylishly reminiscent of the famous "Guernica" by Pablo Picasso, protesting the bombing of that town by the Nazis during the Spanish Civil War. Mr. Zotti's choice of the mural and abstract form, using distorted images with scattered hands and feet tainted in sombre colours, sadly depicts the anguished confusion and absurdity of what took place and how it was being processed at the time in the minds of many people. Like Picasso, the artist is raising his brush in demonstration against the senseless carnage and brutality of war. The seemingly disconnected juxtaposition of unintelligible faces and parts of the human body not only depicts the awful physical impact of war but also symbolizes the breakdown in communication and mutual unwillingness to understand each other.

Commentary on "September 11"
a poem by Cynthia Pearson

The atrocity
Of terror
Fell on
Huge towers
Of concrete,
Crumbling
Into debris.
Falling,
They broke bones,
And soft flesh
Rip on steel,
Into a mangled heap.
Shell shocked
Witnesses
Scream…
The victims
Cry,
Whimper,
Then die,
Falling,
Crashing
Headlong
Into the abyss.
Rummaging
Through the carnage
Loved ones
Picked up
The fallen
Shattered pieces.

Fig. 1-9: Violin on a Rock by Alfredo Zotti

Commentary on "Violin on a Rock"
by Samuel Mann

The artist's inclusion of this real-life composition (Fig. 1-9) in solid three-dimensional form is curiously interesting since one's first reaction is "Why didn't he paint or draw it?" Since there are, to some extent, traces of Picasso's influence in Mr. Zotti's works, one is tempted to recall the famous Spanish painter's own portrayal of the violin in several of his pieces. So what is so special about this instrument? Many lovers of classical music would have no difficulty at all in responding. Regarded as the most important musical instrument in history, the violin is well-known among the repertoire of its family of stringed or bowed instruments, and its alluring shape is, not without obvious reasons, sometimes compared to that of a woman.

Here, the artist appears to be making a statement about music, which in his own perspective as a talented musician himself, is best exemplified by the violin, a musical instrument that is in itself a work of art and, therefore, need not be compulsively reproduced on canvas or paper. In some respects and in other words, what he is saying is that it is the equivalent of a sculpture, and like many of the magnificent wonders that form part of our natural environment, it is to be repeatedly admired. That there is much sentiment expressed in this display, there can be no doubt. It is as if it is almost a painting. The two rocks against which it reclines testify to the robust foundation of the violin's unique place in our musical evolution into today's world.

Commentary on "Violin on a Rock"
a poem By Cynthia Pearson

Even among the crowd of revellers,
Sad and alone on the bandstand,
His song was hard hitting, the strings
Of the violin screaming deceit.

The shrillness of the fiddle wailed,
So many lies told under the stars,
For he had been bewitched by her scent,
And he had played her his song.

The music stopped when she left,
His heart turning cold as a rock.
There he had suspended his song,
While the crowd of revellers played on.

Fig. 1-10: The Depression Trap by Alfredo Zotti

Commentary on "The Depression Trap"
by Samuel Mann

"The Depression Trap" (Fig. 1-10) is configured in such a way that it looks like a device inside of which someone is caught. To the artist, who admits to being bipolar, depression is a subject of intimate concern because of the commonly misunderstood way it is perceived, not only as a stigma, but also in terms of its functional purpose in life. Contrary to what many people think, it is not a disease in Mr. Zotti's well-researched opinion, but a normal phenomenon in human beings as a form of defence mechanism and adjustment to one's environment. Many famous artists and celebrities have been known to be affected by it. One cannot help but notice the salient use of shapes and lines to create a geometrical and structured configuration of confinement. However, there is much more to it than just shapes.

Blue is invoked with faint touches of green here and there to set the mood. The dark colour inside the main compartment where the lonely individual is isolated describes the feeling of hopelessness.

White can be interpreted in two ways: 1) the colour of the prescriptive antidepressants administered to the patient to which he or she becomes addicted or 2) the ray of hope at the end of the tunnel, which connects to the green triangle suspended outside like a magical broom that signifies the renewal of life.

The face of the victim inside the box is, not surprisingly, sad and confused, with eyes out of sync, tearful ears, and raised eyebrows. The fingers or feet ambiguously tell us that he or she could be prostrated or desperately seeking our attention. Mark Goulston, prominent American psychiatrist and author of *Get Out of Your Own Way: Overcoming Self-Defeating Behavior* (1996), says of depression, "There's a saying, when you're in your own mind you're in enemy territory. You leave yourself open to those thoughts and the danger is believing in them."

Commentary on "The Depression Trap"
a poem by Cynthia Pearson

I am caught in a tangled web of lies,
That I will not get out of this prison.

The walls are thick, the heat is intense,
And the guard at the gate stands to watch,
The keys dangling in his hands.

Though the light tries to penetrate the dark,
It's not enough to clear my mind,

My mind is a fog, anyway, and my eyes
Grow dim with each passing day.

And I hear the voices convincing me
To give up, that it makes no sense to fight...
The tunnel is deep and I shall not rise.

Within the blur, I felt a psalm rising
From within, that I should lift up my eyes

To the Light on the green hills without a city wall.
Could this be my help from this trap?

Fig. 1-11: Colours of Emotions by Alfredo Zotti

Commentary on "Colours of Emotions"
by Samuel Mann

"Colours of Emotions" (Fig. 1-11) is a crystal-like impression of the variety of human emotions. The preponderance of blue in all its many shades depicts a varying sense of sadness and coldness, yet at the same time rendering to us a soothing theme of unity and quietness. There is in each glimpse of colours reflected a yellow spark of life, sober brownness, the freshness of nature's ecology, purity, and enlightenment, partially hidden and shared among others and, of course, the deep dark secrets of the emotions.

Mr. Zotti's floral arrangement of the colours is not all perfectly harmonious and remains true to the unpredictable fragility of the emotions in the way some of the colours are heavily tilted in the foreground. Another perspective that comes to mind is that of a lamp or bunch of candles instead of flowers that perhaps symbolizes the energetic role of emotions in our lives.

This picture also appears on the cover of *Alfredo's Journey: An Artist's Creative Life with Bipolar Disorder* (Modern History Press, 2014).

Commentary on "Colours of Emotions"
a poem by Cynthia Pearson

A bright ray of sunshine
Shatters my fragile cage.
One by one pieces
Splinter before me
Into a spectrum of light.

Gleaming with colours,
Slivers of the crystal rainbow,
Reveal day and night
On clear and frosted glass.

On the brittle layers,
Icicles glisten
With tears from wintry nights,
Yet the warm day glows
With healing and sunlight.

The orange-red crystal
Of passion and anger,
Uncovers my creative drive,
Made fertile with the vitality of nature.

Bursts of yellow shards
Burn bright with joy,
And white hot flames
Purify grains of grit inside.

The shattered cage
On the ground before me
Reflects what is true,
But like a bird, I'm free, soaring
Above the crystal blue, calm as the sea.

Fig. 1-12: The Piano Player by Alfredo Zotti

Commentary on "The Piano Player"
by Samuel Mann

Like "Violin on a Rock," this picture (Fig. 1-12) is another expression of the artist's close relationship with music. In this instance, Mr. Zotti is the subject of his own musical composition where his mind is in deep concentration as he obliquely ponders the next note to be played on the keyboard. The position of the left hand is also very interesting because it seems almost as if it is thoughtfully rubbing the other hand and reflexively mirroring the action of the pianist's mind. This is, undoubtedly, a moment of the creative process being captured by the artist, but portrayed in another role of the artist as musician. Using typically light colours in the background and an overall matted effect to produce an elusive atmosphere, Mr. Zotti surrealistically highlights the connection between what the subject is thinking and the context of his immediate surroundings. This is Sartrean existentialism to some extent, if translated, as the keyboard appears to be sturdily challenging and the shirt, although obviously white, is spotted partially to blend in with the purplish bluish background.

Commentary on "The Piano Player"
by Dr. Krystyna Laycraft

When music sounds, out of the water rise....
When music sounds, all that I was I am....

from "Music Poem," by Walter de La Mare

In this painting (Fig. 1-12), you look attentive and immersed in your thoughts. You are probably waiting for the insight into your new composition. Your hands are relaxing and patiently waiting to play these new tunes.

Fig. 1-13: The Boat People by Alfredo Zotti

Commentary on "The Boat People"
by Samuel Mann

"The Boat People"(Fig. 1-13) is a timely painting of Syrian refugees desperately fleeing on the ocean from their war-ravaged home, despite the risk of drowning. Danger in the form of darkness, storm gathering clouds, and a vigorously portrayed sea are contrasted with the bright, foamy crescent-shaped waves, spotted star-like water sprays in the air, and rays emitting from a searchlight on the boat. The predominant use of white and shades of blue suggests a feeling of hope and renewed life awaiting the boat's passengers, who are anxiously holding their breaths out of fear and uncertainty. It reminds us of one of the paintings by the posthumously-famous and post-impressionist Dutch artist Vincent Van Gogh, entitled "Starry Night." Whereas in Van Gogh's painting the turmoil is abstract, personal, and entirely symbolic, in "The Boat People," the subject is more collective and centrally positioned, an insane experience, which although temporary, is one they will never be able to forget.

Commentary on "The Boat People"
a poem by Cynthia Pearson

Boat People
Packed tighter
Than sardines,
Trying to escape
The terror
From the East
And Africa,
The boat people
Hope to survive
Migration, crossing
Perilous seas.
Daring not to breathe,
Vessels burdened
With pain carry
Desperate men and
Women clutching
At the last straw.
Some barely make it
To unfriendly lands.
Hundreds are washed
Ashore like debris.

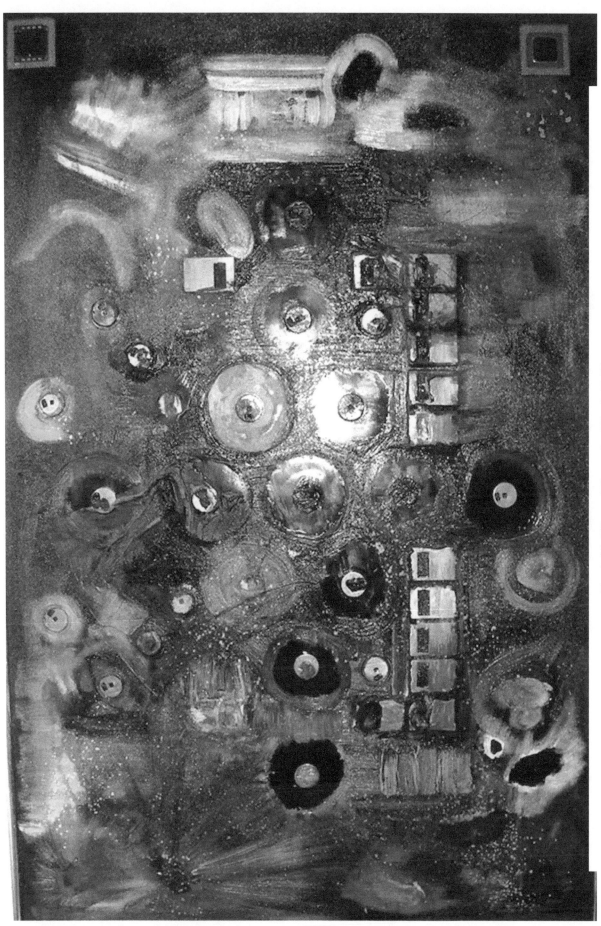

Fig. 1-14: Bits and Pieces by Alfredo Zotti

Commentary on "Bits and Pieces"
by Samuel Mann

"Bits and Pieces" (Fig. 1-14) is a provocative abstract work of art. Many of the pieces appear metallic, but they are, in fact, computer discs and other parts assembled together. The black circular discs could very well be 45s or LPs from the previous century while the neatly stacked rectangular floppy discs on the left suggest that they could be keys of a keyboard. There is a certain shiny, underwater impression, as if the pieces are all lying at the bottom of the ocean, perhaps discarded and left there for quite some time to give us a feeling of obsoleteness. Is the artist trying to tell us something about music and technology? If so, what is the connection? Food for thought, yes, but if one were to step back a bit away from the bits and pieces, one might see that the bigger picture is really a struggle between art and science.

As T.S. Eliot wrote in his immortal "The Love Song of J. Alfred Prufrock," "And would it have been worth it, after all...." With all the changes and transformation made possible by science, would it have been worth it when we look back and recognize that they were all transient and expendable, unlike some of the things intrinsically and permanently embedded in art such as compassion, morality, ethics, and the humanism of mankind.

Commentary on "Bits and Pieces"
a poem by Cynthia Pearson

Man's inventions
On the cutting edge
Past and present,
Metallic discs
That once spun a tale,
Are useless relics
Piled high on top
Of Mother Earth.
Barrenness screams,
As man's progress
Chokes her
To the core,
For as he spits out
Modern inventions
Today,
He discards them
Tomorrow
Into a fossilised dump.

Fig. 1-15: Yesterday, Today, and Tomorrow, the Flowers h by Alfredo Zotti

Commentary on "Yesterday, Today and Tomorrow, the Flowers" by Samuel Mann

Flowers are known to play a traditional role in our lives. We use them to symbolize how we feel on occasions, for example to a loved one or in memory of a relative who has passed away. In "Yesterday, Today and Tomorrow, the Flowers,"(Fig. 1-15) the message of the artist is conveyed in the flowers and their mixed variety of colours.

The dominant purple, which like all the other colours merge into the background, stands for both past and present and is normally associated with accomplishment, success, pride, dignity, peace, and admiration. Mr. Zotti has elsewhere resorted to this same colour in two other paintings relating to his father and himself.

Green, as we know, represents renewal and growth. It also indicates health and prosperity. Thus, it is the present.

Blue and white are expressive of hope, inspiration, dreams, purity, and innocence, all of which can be recognized as pointing towards the future or tomorrow.

Overall, a reflective element and continuity are pervasive throughout the painting. Note the reflection of the light on the vase and the way the vase and the flowers are mirrored in the background and foreground as well. The flowers, in particular, seem to unfurl like smoke on to the window curtain. "Yesterday, Today and Tomorrow, the Flowers" is simply reminding us in a meditative sense that we are all interconnected with one another, the planets, the stars, and the entire universe.

Commentary on "Yesterday, Today, and Tomorrow, the Flowers" a poem by Cynthia Pearson

You were, you are, and always will be
Beautiful, brightening the darkest days,
Soft white petals like silk brushed against
The skin, freshly picked, sun-kissed.
Helenium, lavender, rose, red velvet tones,
Forget-me-not, sit delicately in a pearly pot.

You were, you are and always will be
So pretty, cheering up dreary nights,
Your perfumed scent brings such joy
To pink ribbons tied around a bald head,
Little Mary smiling from that antiseptic bed
To receive morning glory, heaven's delight!

You were, you are and always will be
All to me: a bloom clutched nervously,
To a beaming bride joining the happy groom,
A fresh wreath placed on a solemn tomb.
Yet, you always stay fragrant and true
Whether times are bright or the deepest blue.

Fig. 1-16: Venice by Alfredo Zotti

Commentary on "Venice"
by Samuel Mann

"Venice" (Fig. 1-16) is the aptly chosen cover art for this book. First of all, if you have ever visited that city and you are an art lover, you will agree with me when I say it is perhaps the most beautiful place ever built by man. It is a truly amazing spectacle. And the way Alfredo introduces it like a harbor, it is as if we are actually arriving at the city by boat. The colours with their varying shades of blue, grey, brown, and green (and if one looks hard enough, there is even purple) cast a therapeutic glow on the visitor. It is raining. Incidentally, that is how I remember Venice. But the rain also serves an integral purpose in the composition because as another manifestation of water, which appears to be the subtle theme of the painting, it purifies and cleanses us. The tall lampposts, along with the beacons and towering spires in the background, give us hope and strength. We feel a sense of welcome and offering of service with the empty tables and chairs awaiting us. After all, this is what art therapy is all about.

Commentary on "Venice"
a poem by Cynthia Pearson

I lie back, comfortable and warm in bed,
While Venice Square is awash in sheets of
Ice-blue rain, the lights from the lamps
Cast a yellow glow from their glass casing.
Refusing to be caught in the heavy rainfall,
I huddle at the entrance of my hostel,
Trying to go outside, but not for a swim.
Under the marquee I stood watching teens
Clad in black raincoats wading in the Square,
Giggling loudly as they make a splash, their
Laughter bouncing about the dreary place.
Smiling men rolled up their jeans, discarding
Their boots while they sat near a café,
The rising water claimed their drowning
Knees and feet beneath them. Retreating
Inside, I hurried back to my room, warm and
Dry, not wanting a wet Venetian adventure.
I think I will wait when the East rises with
A promising glow at dawn tomorrow.

Fig. 1-17: The Shore by Alfredo Zotti

Commentary on "The Shore"
by Dr. Krystyna Laycraft

"My soul is full of longing for the secret of the sea."

H.W. Longfellow

Through this painting, you express your longing for the sea, which brings you relaxation, solitude, and calmness. The sea inspires you. The movement of waves gives you not only energy but also refreshment that comes from rhythmic sounds of waves crashing on a sandy beach. Sitting on the sandy beach, touching water with your feet, you are able to think about your new project, new poem, and new song.

PART II-
The Impact of Art Therapy

Chapter 2 -
Creative Writing as Therapy
by Bob Rich, PhD

I was born when the bombs were falling. As my mother was holding me for the first time, on the ground floor of a hospital, a plane crashed into an upper storey. Mother didn't know whether the hospital would collapse. So, she got a nurse to sew her up—there were no anaesthetics or even analgesics available—then walked for three hours, carrying me, through the deep snow of Hungarian February. She took three months to recover from that walk.

As a toddler, I lived in the ghetto. For the first two years of my life, the adults caring for me were constantly terrified. An infant can't yet understand language, but does take in emotion. To have the giants who love you radiate despair and helplessness is the ultimate in trauma. Tiny children can only protect themselves in one way, by shutting off all emotion, so that's what I did. For perhaps half of my life, the only two emotions available to me were anger and sadness. I could react with fear to a physical danger, but anxiety, happiness, joy, the full range of human emotions, were what I observed in others, and understood in an intellectual way, but had no gut feeling for.

Even today, after extensive self-therapy, my version of emotions is a 1920s black and white movie with subtitles instead of the Technicolor emotions of others.

A concomitant of this way of being is poor visual imagery. So, whether it is a chess game, a map, or an emotional maelstrom, I perceive it in words, and express it in words. Paradoxically, this has made my writing very visual and passionate, or at least that's what people tell me. I just write what comes.

From about five years of age, I was subjected to systematic emotional abuse. Every instant, I fought my stepfather, while at the same time, I internalized his abuse. For example, until I was twenty-one, my assessment of myself was, "If there is a wrong way of doing it, or even if there isn't, I'll do it that way first." I had forgotten, or repressed, that this was a literal translation of his statement about me, often said in my hearing.

As a result, as a teenager and young man, I would have qualified for the diagnoses of Post-Traumatic Stress Disorder (PTSD), and major depression. I didn't know this, just knew that I was stupid, and ugly, and useless, and that no one could possibly love me.

The first antidepressant I found was study, and reading generally. I devoured books, and thought about them, and, as a result, was way ahead of my schooling in knowledge, mental skills, and understanding. I was doing mental multiplication of two-digit numbers while my classmates were learning the two times table. By seventeen years of age, I'd read all the books in my school library, and the local public library, even including Shakespeare's complete works and the Bible. A friend once described me as a walking encyclopaedia because of my great store of readily-retrieved, useless information.

At eleven years of age, I discovered the benefits of running. Vigorous exercise proved to be a great antidepressant. Once I burst through the pain barrier, I entered a state of not-thinking, not-feeling, being in a higher place, true meditation. So I became addicted to distance running, training for thirteen days out of fourteen, covering 100 miles per week. I usually set myself a problem before going on a run, such as a University assignment. After I recovered from the run, it was usually there in my mind, ready to be written down.

For years, I didn't know I was creative because all my creativity was invested in science. My first apprenticeship in writing was scientific reports, in which I departed from the traditional stodge and insisted on simple, understandable language. This expanded to explanatory "how to" articles and letters when I worked as a Research Scientist for the CSIRO, Australia's major research organization. In 1980, I started writing for *Earth Garden* magazine, and suddenly acquired a wide following. I expanded to fiction in 1986, and my skills have continuously blossomed since.

I got rid of my PTSD (without knowing I had it), and gained control over my depression, between twenty-one and twenty-three years of age. I cured my depression at forty-three, in 1986, and writing fiction had a part in it. I've described the way I made these achievements in my novel, *Ascending Spiral*.

When I write, I create one or more people, a reality for them to live in, and present them with challenges. From then on, I seem to channel rather than invent. I am *in* that reality, and *am* the person from whose point of view I write.

Didn't Walter Mitty do the same thing?

So, the most immediate, easiest, and least useful benefit of creating stories (whether they are written down or not) is a holiday from a bleak life, into another reality that's at least partly under my control.

Second, much of the time, I practice mindfulness. When I do anything, I consciously and deliberately do *that* thing and focus all my attention on it. Thinking only hurts if you do it. The 1001 activities of daily life are all opportunities for meditation.

This is why writing fiction is such good therapy. Any other creative activity will do the same, even cleaning house can be creative: it converts mess into a space of beauty and welcome. However, writing is *fun*. Might as well make meditation enjoyable!

The third benefit is deeper, more powerful, and has ongoing benefits. My early writing had a theme: just retribution, the victim conquering the bully. My first published fiction was a historical series that involved physically and numerically smaller forest dwellers defending themselves from genocidal attacks by nomads. During the thirty years of warfare, they were forged into "The Mother's sword, to defend the wild places, and to fight slavery and injustice anywhere." My first short story collection was *Striking Back from Down Under*, very different content, the same message.

I started writing stories with the aim of a second anthology, to be called *Criminal Justice*, but ended up with only four short stories. My interest had changed to compassion, reforming, rather than punishing the aggressor. The years of writing were my therapy, moving me beyond the need to strike back.

The greatest issue facing me currently is the coming mass extinction on planet Earth, which will include humanity. We are now past the tipping points. Nothing can prevent a huge disaster, as bad as, or perhaps worse than the end of the Permian period, 250 million years ago, during which 96 percent of then extant species died out, and it took over 10 million years before the ecosystem showed signs of recovery.

This is not the place for stating my evidence. All that matters is that I honestly believe it. The result: my last three novels have focused on issues like: Can love reform a person so traumatized he wants to kill everyone? How should we live in the face of coming disaster? Is there meaning, even if all humans die?

So, once more, writing is therapy. My therapist is not another psychologist, but a whole band of people I've invented, and who teach me.

It so happens that those who read my books like the products of my imagination. My books have won awards and prizes, and I get wonderful reviews. However, this actually doesn't matter. What matters is that my writing is my growing edge, the place where I heal.

Chapter 3 -
A Dream Come True!
by Victor Paul Scerri

I am writing this article to share a unique experience that led me to consider the idea that teaching with a pompous attitude can sometimes lead to a life-changing career decision. I recently moved to the Island of Porto Santo, which is located forty-one Nordic miles from its sister island of Madeira, in the mid-Atlantic Ocean, off the West Coast of Africa. This is a place where sea breezes are warmer than the ocean currents, and the weather is springtime like all year round. Most apartments here in Porto Santo face the south. Mine is no exception. The morning after I arrived, well rested, I opened the balcony window to peer at the sea-view. Passing couples, cyclists, and jogging enthusiasts inspired me to take a stroll across to the other side of the road, which is just a few meters from the beach.

I sat on my towel and watched a man windsurf through a red, orange, and yellow glow that rippled in the morning horizon. In a trance-like mode, I felt the bubbles from the incoming ocean tide rolling over and in between my toes, and my feet sunk into the golden fossil sand. In the distance was the whisper of a surfer on his surfboard. He sailed the waves towards me and stopped close to where I sat.

Picking up his surfboard under his arm, he said, "It is wonderful to ride the waves at this hour of the day," and with a grin, he added, "and before I face the school hustle and bustle."

"Are you a teacher?" I asked.

"Yes, my name is Paulo, and I teach English classes in the eleventh grade. Three groups of seventeen students studying various subjects: art, computer science, and history."

"My name is Victor Paul," I replied. "Thinking back, I wanted to be a teacher. However, that was not to be."

"Why?"

"Well, to keep a long story short, I studied at the Medway College of Art in England where I achieved a second place in a precious award-winning oil painting competition. During the third and final year, my teacher looked at a portrait I was working on and said, "A camera could produce the same results. It has no soul." I just did not understand how the art teacher could speak to me in front of all the students in such an insulting tone. I was considered a gradient (a) student. I felt ignorant and incapable of comprehending, that is until I travelled to Japan.

"In Tokyo, I rented a flat in Roppongi Hills, for nine months. During my stay there, I was engrossed in haiku poetry, Zen Calligraphy, arts and crafts and cultural traits.

"For the first time in many years, I was inspired to paint. I touched upon a method of painting—and possibly a lost secret—producing two images blindfolded. One image was of an ape and another of a monkey. Then one morning while walking, I noticed a weather-beaten sign and took a photo. While looking at the photograph, awareness of what my art teacher tried to convey came to light. It was as if the penny dropped. Many years had passed, but nonetheless, I realized the frustration my art teacher must have felt, unable to express his wish to enlighten my inner emotions."

"You are a well-travelled Englishman, are you not?" asked Paulo.

"Well, I have travelled and lived in Norway, driven through Europe many times, and have spent several months in various places around Asia before I came Porto Santo."

"Awesome. My students will soon be thinking about their future employment opportunities or further tertiary studies, and I was wondering if you would consider doing me a big favour."

"What would that be?"

"If you were to share some words of wisdom with my English class, that would surely teach my students something valuable that they could use in the near future."

The next Monday, I went to meet Paulo at his school. I dived right in, and said, "For those of you who are not thinking about what skill to develop by eleven years of age, I can say this: Work is easy! Anyone can work at something. So why not concentrate on the tools of life…education. Sweep the roads and collect the rubbish if that is what it takes. Just continue to study. Although, you should be thinking of an overall skill to stay in university until you're around twenty-five, which will provide new knowledge for your journey. To be able to administrate your goal without assistance is real independence. It will also help to inspire the eventual career move of your choice."

I thought to myself: If I can get one student to listen and change the course of direction to improve the quality of his or her life, then I would be happy that my presence here is meaningful and I have actually helped these young people. The school bell went off. It was the end of class.

"I'll try to arrange for Victor Paul Sherri to come back next week," Paulo said.

The following Monday, at 08:30, I was back at the school. I brought a calligraphy brush, ink, a stone, some driftwood and some *washi* paper, a kind of paper that was invented in Japan using fibres from the bark of the *gampi* tree. The piece of driftwood housed snugly, in a curved part of the wood, the large oval stone, almost as if it were meant to be there.

All eyes from the class seemed to be on my actions. I placed four smaller stones on the washi paper to hold it in place. The paper was about a meter long, thirty centimetres wide, and stretched out on the floor.

One by one, I asked the students to hold the calligraphy brush that I had previously dipped into some ink.

"Look at the object for a short while and then close your eyes," I said. "Now, without too much thought, paint what you believe is similar, keeping your eyes shut."

They laughed at me as if that could not be done.

Over fourteen students made their calligraphy strokes on the paper. With the addition of a little orange colour acrylic, I made some touches on their strokes of black ink. Their young faces were eagerly anticipating with enthusiasm what the result would be. I held up their work of art for all the class to see, at which point I saw them standing still with their mouths open. With my camera, I took a photo of the painting.

"Every good story must have a moral message," I said, and I began to tell the story of my college days, how I left never to return.

"Thirty-five years later, after a visit to Japan, looking at photographs, I realized I had taken a picture of a rusty sign. It was then I realized what the teacher had tried to convey that I failed to understand. Apart from the sign having become a stunning work of art in the photo, it had a powerful message: the rusty metal, with all its weather-beaten corrosion due to winds, storm, tsunami, dryness, and all that it had gone through, had a message I believed—this was a piece of metal that had come from the other side of the world, and because it had been through a lot, it seemed to be alive, bearing the scars of time gone by. This story and its value had been immortalized in the work of art now."

The students were completely silent, and as I showed the collective effort of creating a piece of artwork on washi paper with ink, some begin to understand the sacred importance of the driftwood and the stone that had been shaped by the environment and been through many changes.

The following day, Paulo wrote me an email to say that the students had told him that it was their best class ever.

During my nine months living in Tokyo and travelling the land, I read many books. I read that about 300 BC, monks would roam freely throughout China and Korea and also to and from Japan. In many ways, the monks were teachers and helped society to grow. At this time, Chinese art was a mix of meditation. Japanese monks found the work mystical while the Chinese had little value for this kind of art. Japan has some exhibits that are unique from that period. It's believed there is no other similar art in the world.

For some reason, my mind decided to meditate and photograph a subject that I could engrave in my mind. I just acted on intuition from that moment on. I could then paint without looking, with my eyes shut, simply by retrieving a picture stored in temporary memory. The experience gave me goose pimples. In my mind, I believed I had achieved what the artists did in China around 300 BC. I have no idea why I should come to this assumption because I have never seen a picture from that period. I only read about it. However, I thought I could teach this way of painting; this was the reason why I chose the subject in the school using a piece of driftwood and a stone from the beach.

I came to the conclusion that when we do things spontaneously, without thinking directly, we are guided by our subconscious. The subconscious has a mind of its own, and when we least expect it, it activates our thoughts to do whatever comes spontaneously. I believe many things we do are not dominated by the mind but come from a spiritual awareness that connects with the brain.

Many questions remain unanswered about how the mind works subconsciously and spontaneously, and we need to look further into this phenomenon. I believe we don't understand yet what is going on when it comes to the subconscious. However, it is possible to develop these subconscious abilities and get in touch with our subconscious. But for this, we need to see things from a different perspective: to embrace the idea that we are a part of the Universe, at one with the Universe. And that there are energies that bind us to the whole so that we are really a piece of the puzzle.

The closest I have been to achieving this kind of state of mind and contentment was in Japan. I remember, while visiting a huge park with giant-sized trees, a gardener who seemed to have a monk attitude as he swept fallen autumn leaves in a very wide road. The man had an extraordinarily long wooden broom. He stood holding the broom handle, standing with his back straight, and swung the broom with harmonic movements. The leaves seemed to float in the air effortlessly, landing in the centre of the road. Another person collected the pile of leaves and put them into a container. I could have easily watched the monk sweep the leaves every day. It was kind of mystical, as if the monk were working in a trance-like mode.

My action to paint with my eyes closed was for me to achieve a connection with the self in its spiritual state of mind. I can paint in this way at anytime, relying on my inner self. I capture the moment of thought. They say that the majority of people use less than 10 percent of their brain capacity. I believe we should strive to use more of our brain power, just like some people who suffer with bipolar disorder do.

Fig. 3-1: Painting with my eyes closed – Victor Paul Scerri

Fig. 3-2: The monkey painted with my eyes closed after simple meditation in 2005 while in Tokyo,

Fig. 3-3: The gorilla painted with my eyes closed after simple meditation while in Tokyo, Japan.

References

Curtis, C., Sensei. (2009, March 01). 2009 Shugyo Tassei Kigan Shiki Seminar. Retrieved September 05, 2016, from http://curtissensei.com/wp-content/uploads/2009/03/stks-seminar-ki-breathing-ki-meditation.pdf Linked from post http://curtissensei.com/?p=351

Shute, C. (October 01, 1968). The Comparative Phenomenology of Japanese Painting and Zen Buddhism. Philosophy East and West, 18, 4, 285-298.

Pahl, R. H. (2002). *Breaking away from the textbook: Creative ways to teach world history.* Vol. 2, the Enlightenment through the 20th century. Lanham, MD: Scarecrow.

Chapter 4 -
A Creative Journey
by Krystyna C. Laycraft

"The creativity is the actualization of potentiality,
and the process of actualization is an occasion of experiencing."
— Alfred North Whitehead

In my book *The Courage to Decide* (2015), I wrote about the transitions in my life between different value dimensions. Since my graduation from the Physics Department of the University of Warsaw, right into my forties, I lived in a world governed by *systemic value dimension*. My inner world was characterized by self-direction, persistence, motivation, and commitment. I had long-range plans, and my thinking was analytical. Most of my professional life was cantered on creating mathematical models of complex physical phenomena. I was excited and satisfied with my work, but slowly beginning to feel that I needed something different in my life. A strange feeling of dissatisfaction began to creep in when I started to feel like an insignificant element in a large, sterile system.

I needed a change and became interested in a social world characterized by *extrinsic values*. I became involved in creating different schools and working on many educational projects. For more than a decade, I lived in this extrinsic value dimension. During that time, by interacting continuously with young people, I opened myself to others and learned how to accept and trust people without judgment. I also learned how to enjoy surprises.

However, I began to feel exhausted and needed to gear down my professional life. Fortunately, a close friend of mine, Dr. Helen Diemert, invited me to a series of her lectures on the fundamental arts. I accepted her offer with a great deal of gratitude, and her lectures motivated me to start painting. By escaping to the Rocky Mountains each weekend and immersing myself in creative pursuits, I found the tranquillity I was looking for. I fell in love with the process of being by myself in nature, deeply observing the beauty of mountains, streams, wildflowers, and golden rocks. I found these artistic trips very therapeutic and always returned home energized and fulfilled.

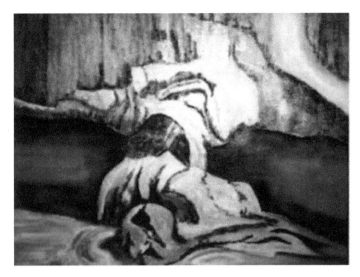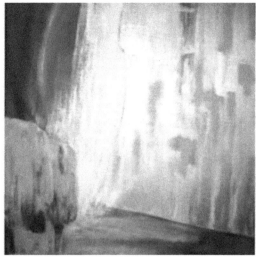

Fig. 4-1: My first paintings (1994/95)

Slowly, I began shifting my interests from the external, social world into an *internal* one. I decided to pass on the running of the school to my family and move to my husband's ranch.

Fascination with Nature

Living on my husband's ranch, I found acceptance, joy, love, solitude, and creativity. During the first few months at the ranch, I was amazed by the beauty of the low hills, immense fields, twisted trees, fragile flowers, clear skies, and warm winds. I simply absorbed everything around me. Instead of seeing, I was *observing*; instead of hearing, I was *listening*; instead of feeling, I was *touching*. I felt such strong surges of energy flowing through my body that I needed to express myself. I started writing poetry and painting nature. I loved surprises and was intuitively searching for the meaning, shape, form, and texture of my surroundings. I was looking for interesting associations of colours—such as golden bales of hay on green fields, silver clouds in navy blue skies, or colourful wildflowers in waving meadows. I felt great joy in painting these special objects of nature or writing poems about them.

"How to Paint Infinity"

August 17, 2003
Sky, blue, gray, navy blue,
Rich in gold clouds,
Sun and moon.
Falling stars, bringing hope for change.
Reflected in standing water.
How difficult it is to paint the universe!
How to paint emptiness?
How to paint infinity?

"The Silence"

September 15, 2003

Silence.
Peace.
I listen through the whole of my body.
And what do I hear?
The breath of a dog,
The rustle of grass.
And again a deep silence.
When it's that quiet,
My eyes get sharp.
And what do I see?
Heavy, black, clouds on the horizon.
Golden patches of
The sun piercing through clouds.
Golden fields and green hills,
A straight path leading somewhere.

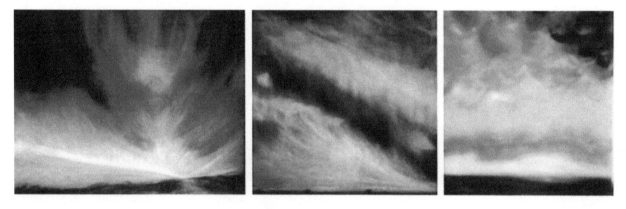

Fig. 4-2: Pastes of skies, (2003/2004)

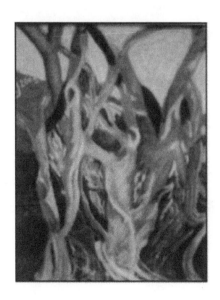 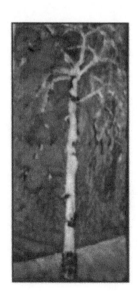 

Fig. 4-3: Acrylics of trees, (2003/2004)

Concentration on Chaos Theory

That year, winter came early and I couldn't go for walks or sketch outside, so I concentrated on preparing a series of lectures on Chaos Theory for artists, students, and the general public. At the same time, I started working on paintings that expressed the concepts of Chaos Theory, using the mixed media techniques I'd learned from Jeanne Krabbendam, an artist from Vancouver.

I worked on this artistic project for almost two years and named it "Journey Through Chaos Theory." It became the solo exhibition at the Art Point Gallery in Calgary. I wrote in the artistic statement, "Over the past two years, I've opened myself up to a variety of experiences by visiting my native Poland, travelling to new places like New Zealand, Singapore, Greece, and Australia, and attending many scientific conferences. Some exhibitions, talks, and images caught my attention and became bifurcations[1] of my creation. The dynamics of human life have their evolutionary trajectories and can be described by their attractors.[2] In my artistic work, I've examined people's actions, which usually draw towards the six chaotic attractors: freedom, love, pleasure, power, knowledge, and longevity."

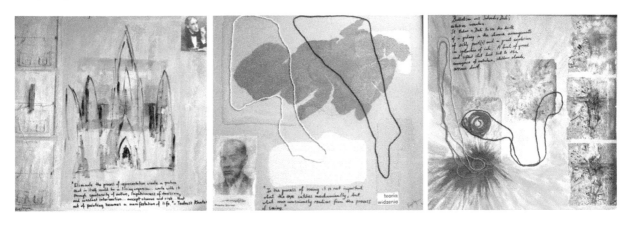

Fig. 4-4: Paintings of bifurcations: Triptych of Kantor, Strzemiński, Dali, (2004/2005)

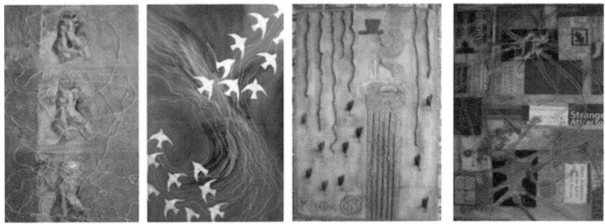

Fig. 4-5: Paintings of attractors of love, pleasure, power, and knowledge, (2004/2005)

I hoped my lectures and paintings on Chaos Theory would help people understand themselves better. I taught them to be sensitive to nuances, to accept unpredictability, and to favour instability over equilibrium.

---

[1] Bifurcation – a point of branching into new types of behavior
[2] Attractor – the characteristic behavior of a dynamic system

Interest in Individuation

Later, I concentrated on Jung's concept of individuation. He defined individuation as the establishment of a right relationship between the ego—"who I think I am," and the Self—"all that I *really* am." During the first half of our lives, we construct and maintain a persona-mask, which is nothing more than our adaptation to the conditions of social existence. The construction of a workable persona is a necessary part of human development and enables us to function effectively within society. It's our titles, our functions, our duties, our roles, but not *really* us. We need a great deal of psychic energy to maintain this identity structure. Very often, we become so rigid we forget to live fully and honestly. The main goal of individuation is to free our ego from its identification with persona and to immerse ourselves in the chaos of genuine living (Jung, 1971).

I was so interested in the concept of persona that I decided to create a painting expressing it. For many days, I didn't know how to do it. Finally, I dreamt that I was hiding behind some large trees. This was the starting point for my painting. I painted myself behind those trees with a clothesline drawn between them. Along this line, I hung the discarded masks of myself from different periods of my life. This meant I didn't need them anymore, and it allowed me to immerse myself in the "chaos of genuine life."

Fig. 4-6: Persona, Mixed Media, (2005)

Contemplating *I Ching*

For the next few years, I immersed myself in contemplations on the *I Ching*. It is the greatest Chinese classic ever written and became the foundation of both the Taoist and Confucian philosophies. The *I Ching* delineates a system of archetypal symbols called hexagrams. Hexagrams depict every possible human situation as a sequence of continual transformations from chaos to order and again from order to chaos.

For me, contemplating the *I Ching*'s sixty-four hexagrams was like going through an entire human life and experiencing a variety of life situations. These might include overcoming difficulties, breaking bad habits, experiencing meditative states, making decisions, experiencing powerful emotions, and being creative. To acquire a better understanding of hexagrams, I created sixty-four collages and applied to them some of my own nature photographs taken while journeying through many different countries.

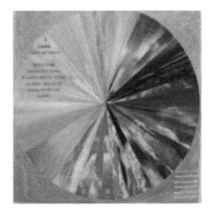  

Fig. 4-7a: Twelve examples of collages of hexagrams:
#1. Creative, #14 Inner Wealth, #16 Enthusiasm,
#22 Grace, #23 Splitting Apart, #26

Fig. 4-7b Twelve examples of collages of hexagrams:
Major Restraint, #43 Breakthrough, #34 Great Strength, #13
Fellowship, #33 Retreat, #40 Liberation, #17 Following, (2008/2009)

Fascination with the Theory of Positive Disintegration

Next, by studying the psychological theories of Rogers, Maslow, Piaget, and others, I tried to understand the role of creativity in psychological development. Finally, I found Dąbrowski's Theory of Positive Disintegration, which gave me insights into the secrets of creativity with respect to psychological growth. I was fascinated with his theory and surprised with its similarity to some of the key ideas of Complexity Science. Dąbrowski stressed the importance of "emotional turbulence" in the process of transition from the lower to higher levels of mental life, which complies with the idea of dynamic systems theory where chaos (variability, instability, and unpredictability) is an inherent part of development.

Dąbrowski's (1972) theory leads to the understanding of creative people and their inner psychological conflicts. Creative people display symptoms of increased psychic excitability, nervousness, and psychoneuroses. On the one hand, increased psychic excitability is one of the basic causes of inner tension and conflicts within oneself and one's environment. On the other hand, this increased excitability creates a condition for a broader, deeper, and more complex pattern of experiences. Nervousness and psychoneurotic symptoms are necessary forms of human growth and signs of the beginning of an advancing process of positive transformations.

While studying Dąbrowski's (1996), theory I created collages expressing the five levels of positive disintegration: (1) primary integration, (2) unilevel disintegration, (3) spontaneous multilevel disintegration, (4) organized multilevel disintegration, and (5) secondary integration.

In these collages, I applied fragments of Polish paintings such as those created by Zdzisław Beksiński, Jerzy Duda Gracz, Wojciech Weiss, and Jacek Malczewski. I spent a lot of time searching for images that accurately expressed the emotions and behaviours of people on these levels of positive disintegration and, to my surprise, I found them in the paintings of these artists.

Secondary Integration

A new organization and harmonization of personality.
Self-aware, self-chosen, and self-affirmed structure

Organized Multilevel Disintegration

Increasing stabilization of the hierarchy of values.
Openness, sensitivity, and identification with others.

Spontaneous Multilevel Disintegration

Extensive differentiation of mental structure.
Increasing role of inner conflict "what is" vs. "what ought
to be"

Unilevel Disintegration

Changeable feelings, circular pattern of thought.
Conformity to external standards.

Primary Integration

A narrow, rigid, automatic mental structure.
No internal conflict, but often external conflicts.

Fig. 4-8 Collages of the five levels of positive disintegration, (2012).

Studying the Creativity of Young People

I continuously asked myself why I felt so great when I was painting, arranging collages, or taking photographs. Why did these creative activities give me so much energy? Why am I constantly attracted to new artistic projects? Finally, with all my knowledge and experience, I decided to write my doctoral thesis on the development of creativity in young people.

Creativity is a complex phenomenon, and understanding it requires analysis from many different perspectives. Applying Ken Wilber's integral theory (2008), creativity can be studied from four major perspectives---the subjective (intentional), inter-subjective (cultural), objective (behavioural), and inter-objective (social).

My creative pursuits helped me complete this intellectually demanding project. During my theoretical research on creativity, I created four collages expressing the four perspectives of creativity and ten collages expressing the characteristics of the participants in my study. By selecting and combining a variety of images for my collages, I had time to think, analyse, and deeply understand the creativity and psychological development of young people.

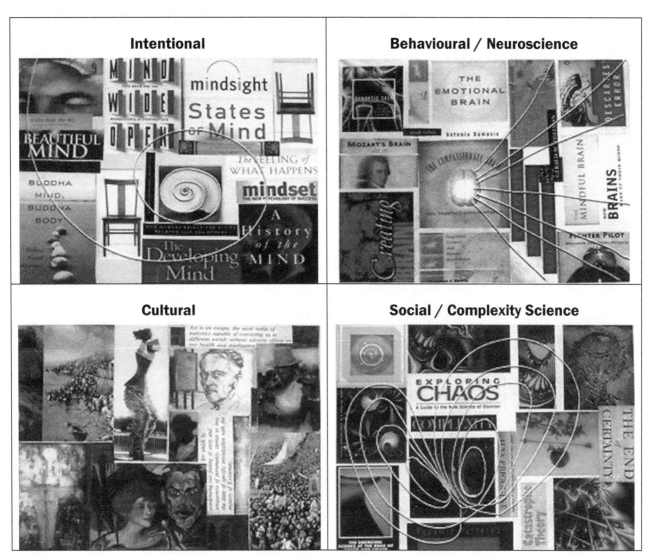

Fig. 4-9: Collages – Four Perspectives of Studying Creativity (2012)

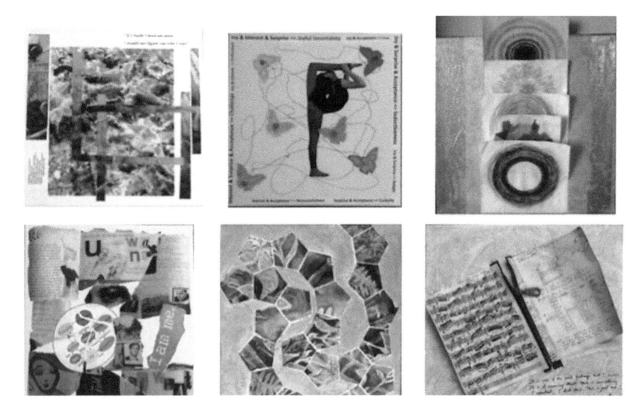

Fig. 4-10 Collages representing the six participants of my study: Stephanie—The Scuba Diver, Krista Jennings—The Contortionist, Eton—The Spiritual Artist, Jade—The Art Teacher, and Alasdair MacEwan—The Young Composer (2012)

I especially enjoyed creating a collage on cultural perspectives. Because I was born and educated in Poland, most of the images I chose for this collage were from paintings and sculptures of my favourite artists—the ones who had influenced me during my adolescence. At that time, I was fascinated with the art and philosophy of Witkacy (Stanisław Ignacy Witkiewicz).

When I was working on this collage, my memories took me back to the time at university when we had discussed Witkacy's ideas. Witkacy claimed that art is an expression of "metaphysical feelings." For him, metaphysical feelings were the most important of all human experiences. Witkacy had been deeply pessimistic that mechanical changes in social development might detract from metaphysical feelings and cause the obliteration of individual creativity (Micińska, 1990).

In some symbolic way, in order to assure him that we still experience "metaphysical feelings" and that individual creativity did not disappear, I honoured him by creating this collage. In it, I included his famous statement, "Art is an escape, the most noble of narcotics capable of conveying us to different worlds without adverse effects on our health and intelligence.... Art which by condensing our feeling of unity and uniqueness of personality, carries us into the state of specific intoxication with the mystery of Existence." (Micińska, 1990)

Fig. 4-11: Collage of Culture Perspective of Creativity, (2012)

My study shows that creativity has many functions in the lives of young people:

- Becomes a way to escape from unfriendly or brutal environments.
- Becomes an outlet for internal tensions and conflicts.
- Promotes conditions that are optimal for the prevention of serious mental disorders.
- Allows them to learn about themselves and connects them to something meaningful.
- Introduces purposes and values in their lives.
- Empowers them to make life choices that bring joy, satisfaction, and fulfilment.
- Helps adolescents find their future goals and plans.
- Helps young people develop cognitively, emotionally, and spiritually.
- Promotes the growth of resourcefulness, optimism, confidence, and pride.
- Creativity reinforces sensitivity, not only to human issues but often to wider problems of the natural world.

Writing Books

After finishing my graduate studies and defending my doctoral dissertation, I became fascinated with language and wanted to express myself by writing. I knew it would be a very challenging task because English is not my first language. But I tried, and in a few months, I wrote my first book, *Creativity as an Order through Emotions* (2013). In this book, I included a conceptual model of the creativity of young people using the metaphor of a growing tree.

The Integral Creativity

Bloom, amplify, intensify, spread, rise, strengthen, flourish, produce, create.

The Vertical Creativity

Shoot, burst, rouse, liberate, Stimulate, accelerate, inspire, perform

The Horizontal Creativity

Nurture, nourish, support, maintain, sustain, encourage, motivate, teach, explain, clarify, simplify by others.

Fig. 4-12: A conceptual model of the creativity of young people

At the bottom of this model sits *horizontal creativity*, which emerges during late childhood and early adolescence. Metaphorically, it is *the seed* of the tree. It is the beginning of all creative potentiality. Young individuals are searching for new and unknown experiences, which are linked to the emotions of joy, interest, surprise, and curiosity. But their creativity is often impulsive, spontaneous, and superficial. It is characterized by indecision, doubt, and hesitation. Young people oscillate between different interests. During this time, young individuals are highly sensitive to the values, opinions, and expectations of their parents, teachers, and peers. External influences such as those that are supportive, encouraging, accepting, as well as those that are challenging, stimulating, and inspiring, play a decisive role in transitioning them to higher levels of creativity.

The next level is *vertical creativity*. It can be compared to the *stem* of a young tree, which pushes the growth of the tree vertically. This period is characterized by endless experimentation and psychological "awakenings." Young individuals open themselves up to new experiences. They become critical observers of their thoughts, feelings, and behaviours. Through creative activities, they learn about themselves and then connect to something that is meaningful to them. The inner openness enhances their ability to open to others. Young individuals generally want to share their creative products with others.

The transition from vertical creativity to *integral creativity* requires further intellectual and emotional growth. Integral creativity can be likened to *the crown* of a young tree. It is characterized by openness to the external world, sensitivity to others, and developing relationships of love and friendship. Integral creativity is connected with the global process of identity formation, and it helps young people integrate their ideas, beliefs, and values into more complex systems. They become the creators of their own and unique reality.

When I'd finished writing this book, I sent publishing requests to eight Canadian companies and, to my enormous delight, I soon got a positive response. Rick Mickelson, the editor and publisher of AwareNow Publishing, in Victoria, BC, Canada, accepted my book. Thanks to his persistent work, the book was completed and ready for printing in just four months. Because of his continuous encouragement and support, I have written three more books, *Feeling Life*, *A Journey Through the Lands of Feelings*, and *The Courage to Decide*.

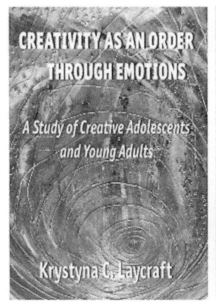  

Fig. 4-13: Krystyna Laycraft's publications (2012-2015)

In *Feeling Life*, I included stories from my adult life, which emerged *through* reflective meditations on my actions, choices, and decisions. I discovered a richness of emotions had been experienced during significant events in my life.

In *The Courage to Decide*, I continued examining my life through the ideas of many philosophers. This process gave me a much better understanding of the decision-making process and its importance in our lives. By making decisions, we trace the path of our lives, direct our psychological development, and define the kind of person we become.

In my book for children, *A Journey through the Lands of Feelings*, I integrated my love for children, passion for telling stories, and enjoyment of creating art, with my imagination, knowledge, and understanding of emotions. This book helps children identify and understand their emotions.

Fig. 4-14 Illustrations for A Journey through the Lands of Feelings (2014)

Conclusion

As you can see from this creative journey, creativity plays many different roles in my life. First, creativity became an outlet for my anxiety and gave me the boost of energy I needed to run a school. Later, my fascination with the natural world prompted me to paint and write poetry. I was trying to capture the meaningful moments and was thoroughly enjoying what I did. The more involved I became in these creative processes, the more satisfied and fulfilled I was.

Finally, creativity became an expression of my images, memories, and experiences. This was a challenging process because I was attempting to express abstract concepts through the medium of art. However, by contemplating, reflecting, and concentrating, I was able to get in touch with my deepest thoughts and feelings. My creativity was then intertwined with the powerful emotions of interest, joy, surprise, love, curiosity, fascination, and hope. Those emotions were the energy that stimulated, organized, and then integrated my thinking and imagination into new understandings.

I can say, without any hesitation, that creativity continues to shape and guide my life. It allows me to learn about myself and others, to connect to meaningful activities, and to understand the true purpose of my life. My creativity is not *fading with age,* but rather, it is deepening and expanding into psychology, philosophy, spirituality, and neuroscience. It inspires me to play with new artistic techniques and new ways of expressing myself.

I cannot predict how far, and in what direction, my creativity will take me next. All I know is the joy and love I experience in pursuing this creative journey.

~ ~ ~

Krystyna can be reached c/o The Center for CHAOS Studies, P.O. Box 549, Nanton T0L 1R0, Alberta, Canada or on the web at www.krystyna-laycraft.com

References

Dabrowski, K. (1972). Psychoneurosis Is Not an Illness. London: Gryf Publications Ltd.

Dabrowski, K. (1996). Multilevelness of Emotional and Instinctive Functions. Lublin: Towarzystwo Naukowe Katolickiego Uniwersytetu Lubelskiego.

Jung, C.G. (1971). *The Portable Jung.* London: Penguin Books

Laycraft, K. (2012). *The development of creativity: A study of creative adolescents and young adults.* Doctoral dissertation, University of Calgary, http://theses.ucalgary.ca/handle/11023/166.

Laycraft, K.C. (2013). *Creativity as an order through emotions. A study of creative adolescents and young adults.* (First edition). Victoria, BC: AwareNow Publishing.

Laycraft, K.C. (2014). Toward the pattern models of creativity: Chaos, complexity, creativity. In Don Ambrose, Bharath Sriraman and Kathleen M. Pierce (Eds.), *A critique of creativity and complexity* (pp.269-290). Rotterdam, Boston, Taipei: Sense Publishers.

Laycraft, K.C. (2014). *Feeling life. Patterns of emotions.* Victoria, BC: AwareNow Publishing

Laycraft, K.C. (2014). *A journey through the lands of feelings.* Victoria, BC: AwareNow Publishing

Laycraft, K.C. (2015). *The courage to decide. The Philosophies on decision-making.* Victoria, BC: AwareNow Publishing.

Micińska A. (1990). *Stanislaw Ignacy Witkiewicz Life and Work.* (Translated by Bogna Piotrowska). Warsaw: Interpress Publishers, pp. 163-164

Wilber, K (2008). *The integral vision.* Boston, MA: Shambhala

Chapter 5 -
"Getting the Hurt in My Head, Out":
The Creative Process and Healing
by Debra Bradley

As a five-year-old child, I was classified as a victim, but now I state without any seeking of pity, I am a sexual abuse survivor. It has been a long journey from victim to survivor, and many people and things have influenced that journey—nothing, however, as much as art and poetry.

This is not a professional paper or an investigative report. There are no academic references nor attached evidence from specialists. This is a personal account of my journey and how I grew into an artist and teacher who can instinctively recognize fellow "victims" in the people I meet. More importantly, this account will touch on how, through the use of creative methods, these individuals can be taught to embrace a new title: survivor.

Most people have heard the sayings "What doesn't kill me makes me stronger," or "The strongest steel is forged in the hottest fire," so why do some victims of abuse survive and, indeed, thrive, while others crumble?

I am far from the only one to have suffered abuse, and others have experienced horrors more horrific than I, so throughout my life, I have wondered why do some grow stronger and survive against all odds, while others seek destructive methods of escape from a life of hellish memories? How did I get here, from that little girl who was repeatedly woken from bedtime dreams, to be subjected to real-life nightmares? How did I grow into this strong woman, a successful mother of three, a grandmother, a teacher, and a compassionate child caregiver who uses art therapy processes with great success? I look back on the path that I have walked, and it has not been a straight and smooth path. There were many twisted bends and moments when I became totally lost. Finding my way has been a long, sometimes sad, often joyous, but ultimately, very creative, journey.

For as long as I can remember, I have utilized various artistic formats to escape, to express myself, and to dream. Pouring paint onto paper, sketching with soft charcoals, manipulating clay, or writing poetry, songs, and stories—all of these and many other creative processes have played a part in my healing and growth. When I became a primary school teacher, these skills came with me.

I love to teach and had always wanted to be a teacher; however, I had not long graduated when I discovered something that was blatantly obvious to all who knew me well. I was never going to "fit" into the system. I could not separate a child's brain from his or her emotions, needs, and wholeness. Delivering intellectual information solely to please the school curriculum in a rigidly structured institution that had little time for creative processes was not for me. I am presently working with young adults whom the school system has failed. These individuals are seen as society's rejects, and nearly all arrive dragging wounded souls and histories of abuse. I am also employed to care for primary-aged children in an out-of-school program. Many of these youngsters are diagnosed as autistic or have a range of special needs. Some have been in care all their short lives, and others are foster children. All of these issues impact on their happiness and emotional wellbeing and all, whether adult or child, need individual care and attention. Using creative processes such as art to engage and connect with an individual who cannot find a way to voice inner emotions is a very powerful tool.

While I do not have an art therapy degree, I have studied art therapy extensively, and more importantly, I have used it to give children a concrete tool, allowing them to express themselves and, as one child put it, "Get the hurt in my heart, out."

I would like to share within this article four very significant examples of "Getting the hurt in my heart, out."

My Personal Story

From the age of five, for approximately two years, a trusted uncle in his twenties sexually abused me. In the dark of the night, he would remove me from my bed and treat me as his "lover." He never physically "hurt" me, so there were no outer marks or bruises for my very loving family to discover. I do not need to go into details; however, I will say that he did to me every act that a man and woman shares, except intercourse, and many other acts that to this day I call "sick." Others may refer to these acts as "kinky," but they will always make me cringe with disgust. He groomed me well, telling me that I was special. He made it clear that bad things would happen if I told anyone about his nightly visits. I remember feeling very confused; he was nice to me in the daytime, treating me with gifts, giving me piggyback rides, and making sure I was treated just like my cousins. I wondered then whether he came to them in the night too. (Later, I found out that he didn't; only I was chosen). On the surface, I was a happy little girl, but inside, I held scars and bruises that would take years to surface.

My uncle suddenly left our city when I had just turned seven. I believe that my grandmother caught him abusing me, although I will never know this as fact, but all the pieces fit. Just because he was physically gone, however, did not end the torment for me. For years after, I feared the night, and when dark fell, I would barricade the door with obstacles—a suitcase or guitar case, or anything that could trip an intruder. I slept with my window locked and my sheets tucked in tightly around me even in the middle of summer. My poor parents just thought I was an insecure little girl as they tried to assure me that the bogeyman was not real. *But I knew he was.*

It was when I was seven that a gifted aunt handed me a pencil and taught me how to draw. This opened doors for me. I could now express how I felt, how hurt I felt inside. I could draw my pain. My mother, who only found out about my abuse when I was an adult, was given many "dark, sad" pictures of tears and broken hearts. I would grab a black crayon and scribble images of shadow-like figures, or put angry slashes of red across a murky background. When I was asked to draw something "pretty," it felt false and unnatural. Inside, I remember feeling ugly, murky, and black; what I was pouring onto paper was me.

I also discovered how to write poetry, and words would flow directly from my heart onto the page. Sometimes, these words horrified my mother. She did not understand how such negative poems could come from such a loved and "happy" little girl. You see, I was two people; the real me was not a good girl because my dreams would be filled with flashes of moments that no child had a right to know about. As I grew older and became aware that I had been sexually abused (before I did not know what to call it), I grew even more afraid. I wrote poems to God, begging him to let me into heaven when I died, but I knew deep down that I was not pure enough for heaven. You see, as a little girl, my uncle didn't "hurt" me. He didn't make me scream in pain. I didn't fight him off, and I will share what so many victims like myself will say with utter shame… sometimes what he did… felt nice, like when someone strokes your back or brushes your hair. This was the hardest thing for me, as it is for many others. I would listen to cases of girls who had been raped and had scars, who screamed when they were touched, and in my head I became the "bad" one, the one who must have had "asked" for sexual attention. It grew darker inside my soul, and I became a promiscuous teenager. I had given up on being good; I could never be loved by God, and I grew angry. I hated each boyfriend even as I "loved" him. I was bitter and usually rejected soon after I fell in love. I turned more and more to my artwork and began writing disturbing poetry. There are not many poems left from those years; only these two remain, one on a scrap of yellowed paper and another in a little book with a broken rusty lock.

I want my teddy,
He is my hero, he is my friend
And if I close my eyes and pretend
In bed at night, there is only teddy and me.

Approximate age: 6 years

Heroes are not real
They are a lie
For girls like me
No knight in shining armour
Will rescue or love a black heart
No angels surround me
Why can't I just die?
Demons taunt me
Even death has no escape
Because only hell waits

Approximate age: 15 years

A friend praised a poem I had written and commented that I had true talent. However, she asked me, "Why don't you write a happy poem?" I tried, but my heart wasn't into nice things. Inside, I was still black and bad...and anything I wrote that was remotely positive felt like a lie. At my hardest points in life when I needed to get the darkness out, I *had* to write or paint. If I locked it in, it would grow in strength and overpower me. Usually, I would feel lighter after I had finished a poem, or I would cry tears of release over a completed artwork. Then I could carry on, as I presented myself as a happy and well-adjusted young lady. As long as I had a pencil at hand, I was okay.

When I became a mother, I continued to paint pictures in secret—ugly art works I shared with no one that expressed my pain and anger (see Fig. 5-1). Most were destroyed immediately after I created them, and it felt good to tear them up into a thousand pieces. A few remained like bad photos that you wished you had destroyed.

Fig. 5-1: This one represents the pain that sexual abuse causes

This artwork is full of imagery. In the right hand top corner, you can see an empty pair of pyjamas discarded on the floor and a window that has only darkness in its frame. It is locked, and there is no escape from within the room. An empty bed is below this, the child taken from its warmth. In the middle of the picture sits a small child, naked, white, shivering, and helpless as it watches an unripened apple cry, plucked too soon from a tree. Hands with bloodstained claws reach for both child and apple and darkness is central to all. In the darkness, you can see close-up segmented features of a man's face, a mouth, a closed eye, a nose.

As an adult, I wrote more sophisticated poetry like this next example. A children's book written for sexual abuse survivors was the "trigger" for this poem.

Like a Part of a Gun

It was a simple trigger...That started it and let it out...
A shell not full of gunpowder but of suffering
And it hit in my heart...A bull's eye
An explosion of anguish
...and my spirit moaned with something worse than nakedness

It hit me with that fatal familiar twist of a dull knife.
Like an adversary, I thought was gone...
Like a betrayal of the worst kind
My heart...opened...and exposed for the entire world to see
My nakedness so abused and my body so misused
An ache, so intense, so bitter, so very familiar, only...stronger
It seems to get deeper and somehow darker.
This forgotten...
...echo of a pain...too strong to ever, really be gone.
And I wanted to curl and whimper
Give in to this passion of darkness
Which had been...
Locked away, stored in a hidden chest covered in tangled chains.
But...The shackles broke
Once again...
And like a hellish bird it struggled, and breathed, liberated
A decomposing breath,
It was free...Once more
I had thought it was faded, softer, stained and weak with age.
But...it had only been hibernating.
It was still there, just waiting for a trigger to escape again.

This time it was a cartoon...just a drawing....
So simple, so innocent, and so pure...not complicated in any way.
An etching of a child curled....in the agony of knowing...
Awareness of things she had no right to identify...
And I recognized her pain
...and I felt it too.
She...just a cartoon...became real
She...just a cartoon...became me
She...just a carton...needed me
...to save her.

But...I couldn't.

I was once again helpless, in the face of something too immense
...too wrong...
Too evil for my God.
Such sadness for...this cartoon child...
Pity for...this heart of mine
And my insides wept with the sheer anguish

And the twist went deep, too bottomless to stop.
I recognized it as soon as it hit...this well-known black hurt...
The tears inside me drowned my soul...threatening to destroy my joy.
But...I grasped it, in a hold of love and strangled the darkness, stopping.
I would not succumb to the helplessness that was....
I am not that little "innocent lost" and vulnerable tiny creature that was...

I am strong now, and though it is not forgotten
I can suppress it
I can embrace that "damage" and wrap "safe feelings" around it
And hide it, stuff it...
Bind its ugly wings and thrust it
...back into its hole
...push that "wound" into its deep dark abyss...and conceal it
...forget that it is there....

But...I know it will escape again, sometime, somehow...
Just a trigger...
Like from a gun.

And though I try so hard not to think too much...
I have to wonder,
...which child will the next bullet hit?

Debbie Bradley, 2013

Throughout my adult years, I became calmer as I realized that I *was* a good person and a light bulb moment caused me to recognize that I had not asked to be abused and that I was in no way guilty of anything. This was the first time I recognized myself as an innocent victim. I had been instructed to find an old photo of myself at five years old and to pretend that this little girl was not me and that she had just come to me and told me about the abuse that was happening to her. I held this little photo to my heart and cried for her until I had no tears left. I chanted over and over, "You poor baby, you poor baby." A weight lifted off me in that moment. I was innocent. The sexual abuse was no longer *my* dirty dark secret—it was my uncle's! I began to talk about it; I no longer had only pencil and paper to get it out.... I could now share it verbally to anyone who cared to listen. How wonderful to be able to discuss how much it hurt! The more I talked, the better I felt, and I realized how soul-destroying it is if you to lock these feeling up, if you have no outlet at all. Thank God I had my creative activities because I do not know how I would have survived my childhood without them.

I had grown into a happy woman and was now an artist who used art to earn a living, and I painted beautiful murals and pretty fantasy lands where all was pure and perfect. My creative outlets continued to help me heal as I embraced a happy and whole life. I then took my next step, and as a mature grandmother, I entered a university, confident and ready to achieve my dream of becoming a teacher. The power of healing with art returned in my first year of teaching.

Fig. 5-2: "I painted beautiful murals and fantasy lands where all was pure and perfect"

**These next stories are all true; however, they have been
changed slightly to protect the students' identities.**

She was only Ten Years Old

A math test was taking place in a classroom where I was assisting. As the teacher read out the
questions, I observed a student getting more and more agitated. She gripped the pencil in a shaking
fist, and it was clear she was about to explode into tears or anger. With an agreed nod, I led her out
of the classroom. After I asked her what was wrong, she burst into tears and refused to answer. I
allowed her to cry for a short time while providing comfort, and then I asked again.

She shook her head and replied, "I can't tell you; he won't let me." It was obvious that she was
too scared to tell me, so I decided to try using art to help her speak. When I asked her whether she
could draw what was wrong, she almost eagerly nodded her head. I gave her paper and pen and she
proceeded to draw an image like this.

Fig. 5-3: "This is the Creeper"

I pointed to the small stick figure and asked "Who is this?" She replied, "Me," and then she
pointed to the large stick figure and said, "This is The Creeper." (The Creeper is the frightening flesh-

eating demon who feasts on humans for twenty-three days every twenty-third spring. See the 2001 film *Jeepers Creepers* and the 2003 sequel *Jeepers Creepers II*.) She pointed to the picture and went on to explain, "He comes to me when I am bad, and he stabs me in the heart." She clarified that she had not done her homework, so she did not know the answers to the math test, so The Creeper was punishing her. It turned out that this little girl had seen the movie *Jeepers Creepers* while sleeping over at a friend's house, and she believed The Creeper was visiting her every night. Being able to draw what was happening to her allowed her suffering to come to light. Her parents were informed, and positive steps were put into place to help her. Drawing her terror separated it from her being and allowed her to speak of the suffering the child on the paper was undergoing.

He was Twelve Years Old

I was invited to deliver an art lesson in a local primary school, and after teaching the children how to find stories in the textured papers they created, I began to illustrate how colour can be linked to emotions. This lesson started with a PowerPoint of colours. Each colour and hue was examined, and children were then encouraged to discuss how the colours made them feel. Sharing their thoughts and ideas, they became very animated as they related times in their lives that linked with the various colours. In the following lessons, they were asked to use paint and paper to represent a moment in their lives that they would call the "worst" and/or the "best." It is interesting that most children are eager to pour their sad or angry emotions onto paper and only turn to the "happy artwork" later, almost as an afterthought. Some never even start a happy picture. It is the bad emotions they *want* to paint.

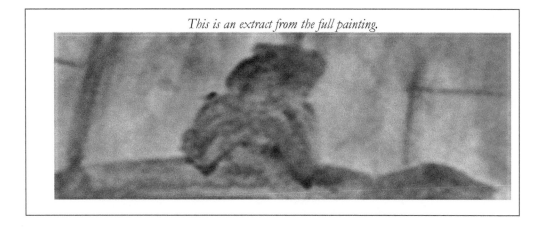

This is an extract from the full painting.

While the children are painting, I walk around the classroom, observing and commenting on each child's work. If the painting is a swirl of yellows and pretty blues, I may say, "That looks like a happy time; can you tell me what is happening?" They usually are quick to share this treasured memory. If, however, the artwork is full of darkness and very obviously holds pain and hurt, I usually softly ask whether they want to tell me what is happening. In most instances, they find it easy to talk about how sad they felt when Grandma passed, or a loved puppy was killed, or how it felt to be bullied. They point to the various colours and talk freely about what is happening on the page. This pain is not a part of them in this moment; it is now "on" the page.... External and once detached, pain is not so difficult to talk about. The child is talking about something outside now, and the audience is looking at the picture, not at him or her.

It was in one of these lessons that a year seven student (I will call him Bobby) painted a picture using murky reds, greys, and blacks. At the bottom of the page was a dark figure kneeling in a position of prayer over another dark figure that was lying flat before it. Above these figures, a larger dark figure was floating upwards, and silhouetted behind this figure was the outline of a young girl with long hair. There was darkness in the corners. It was obviously a much planned artwork full of meaning and executed by a gifted young artist. I asked Bobby whether he wished to tell me what was happening, and he nodded. He proceeded to explain that the dead girl was his sister and the person leaning over her was his father. The dark figure floating away was his mother, who had removed herself emotionally from the once happy family.

He said, "I am mad because all my dad does is cry, and Mum won't talk about it, and I am mad at my sister; that's why there is lots of red; that's my anger.... I am so angry at her because she died and now no one is happy...." Then he added in a very soft voice, "The darkness is me.... I am angry at me...for being angry at my sister for dying." The teacher informed me that his sister had died suddenly a few months ago and he had refused to talk about it; this was the first time he had spoken of her death. A painting had given him a voice. At the end of the lesson, I asked all the students to write a short poem about a chosen artwork.

When I arrived the next week, I was met by an excited teacher. She led me to Bobby's desk eagerly. Bobby proudly produced the poem he had written at the bottom of his art piece.

When I asked him whether he could share his artwork and poem with the class, he proceeded to the front of the classroom and did so.

This class of year sevens held a group of tough little individuals who were not generally known for compassion. However, after Bobby finished reading his poem to the hushed room, one by one, each student stood and quietly surrounded him in a class hug. His mother explained later that this moment was not just the beginning of the long road to healing for Bobby but for the entire family. Art is a powerful and underestimated tool.

> You tore our hearts apart
> With the last beat of your heart
> Our pain has no cure
> If I could see you would I feel?
> Would your face be clear and real?
> You're gone and only tears remain
> But your tears I must not shame
> If only your death was just
> A stupid little game...

Excerpt from a poem written by a 12 year old child.

He was just Eleven Years Old

A young boy had experienced ongoing bullying in his classroom, not by the children but by his teacher. He was now removed from this toxic environment; however, he had changed from a happy little boy, and his mum had asked me to help him express the frustration he was feeling. I helped him create artwork and then guided him as he found the words to express his feelings on paper. When he began working with me, he was shy and withdrawn, and it was hard work to get him to smile or even look at me. It didn't take him long after I provided examples and the tools he needed to produce beautiful artwork (see Fig. 5-5). His outlook on life changed as he grew back into a confident little boy, who was now recognized as an artist and an illustrator. I remember the look of sheer delight on his face as he explained his artwork to me and others. He could not express his excitement quickly enough. Here are some examples of his beautiful art.

Fig. 5-5a: Magical King of the Sea

Fig. 5-5b: "I feel so free..."

BLACK BIRD

Bird, black as the
night sky,
Wherever feathers
touch destruction
follows.
Sucking life.
Intense sadness.
Swirling dangerous
flight.

Fig. 5-5c: Black Bird

Birds are flying through the air
With wings so stretched and wide
Wonder how they dare...
Fly to the sun and tide

Fig.5-5d: "Birds are flying through the air"

Artistic skills are so underused within the educational system, but they can be used to build literacy skills and to teach math, history, science, religion, and all strands of education. They build creativity, while allowing a child to express and share his or her emotions in ways that many children could never do…with just words alone. It is clear in these three examples that art indeed helped these two children and me. However, it cannot be stated explicitly that art will help all.

Was I born creative, or did I become creative through the seeking of healing? I believe that being creative helped me heal and further study has revealed that many "victims" find strength through the creative arts. I use the word victim with distaste because this word signifies weakness and helplessness, with which I refuse to label myself or my clients. We are survivors, and we grasp many different creative processes to express our inner emotions.

Some of my adult clients write music; others draw, and others write. Younger students paint as they express their pain. The ones who have no creative outlet seem to struggle more as they fight to control the "ghosts" of their past. This being said, there is a history of many gifted artists who have suffered severe depression, despite being able to create. Perhaps it has something to do with their environments, those who surround them, for I was embraced by a positive and loving family. Then again, perhaps it is just the strength of the individual.

Perhaps some of us are simply meant to succeed, and no matter what evil befalls us, we will never succumb to the madness abuse causes.

That being said, I end with these questions: Had I been unable to express my pain through art, who would I have become? Would I have embraced myself as a victim, or as the survivor I am?

References

Bath, H. (December 07, 2008). The Three Pillars of Trauma-Informed Care. *Reclaiming Children and Youth,* 17, 3, 17-21.

Cain, T. (2009, May). Addressing Trauma: The First Step in My Journey to Recovery. Retrieved September 5, 2016, from http://www.crisisprevention.com/CPI/media/Media/Blogs/addressing-trauma-the-first-step-in-my-journey-to-recovery.pdf

Rettmann, D. R. (2009, March 1). *Journal of Safe Management of Disruptive and Assaultive Behavior, 17*(1). Retrieved September 5, 2016.

Shea, P. (n.d.). The Role of National Association of State Mental Health Programs Directors in Promoting Trauma-Informed Mental Health Care. Retrieved September 5, 2016, from www.nasmhpd.org

Steele, W. and Raider, M. (2001). Clinician or witness: the intervener's relationship with traumatized children. *Reclaiming children and youth, 17* (3), 44–47.

Chapter 6 -
Why Music Matters:
The Healing Properties of Music Therapy
by Michael Bradley

It is often stated that "music soothes the savage beast." However, this quote is actually a misquote from William Congreve's play *The Mourning Bride* (1697). The actual passage is "Musick has charms to soothe a savage breast," and it is intended to draw a connection between the healing properties of music and the complexity of human emotion. This being said, it is perhaps unfortunate that those who quote, or perhaps misquote, have misunderstood the context of the words. For it is on further examination of the play that one comes upon the lines where the speaker finds himself unable to be reconciled:

> What then am I?
> More senseless grown,
> Than trees or flint,
> O force of constant woe. (Congreve, 1697)

Nevertheless, many have used the arts as a means of recourse during trying times when the stress of everyday life toils upon the psyche (Yun & Gallant, 2010). For some, the means of expression has been through painting, others via the pen to create a literary example of their creativity. My choice was to use music both from recorded artists and composed by myself.

I certainly agree that the genre and tone of the music can hold great influence in the context of human emotions and, to an extent, the ability to reason within such emotions. There are genres of music, often broadcast in shopping malls, that make me want to leave the area immediately. This is generally restricted to what I class as Muzak®, clearly not intended for those who can actually play an instrument.

I have a broad taste in music that ranges from early rock 'n' roll to contemporary alternative, with perhaps country/western and rap being the exceptions. That said, there are times when one needs to choose the genre/artist with care due to the emotions that can be generated via the nexus of mood and music.

Elton John claimed that sad songs say so much, but why is this so? Why is there a predilection towards sombre music or lyrics when one is feeling sad? If you were to enquire, I am sure that most people would prefer to be either happy or, at the very least, neutral in their emotiveness. Would not a happier, more upbeat song be more appropriate in changing one's mood, or to quote Congreve, "soothe the savage breast"?

Yet it is to sad songs that we turn when our mood turns toward the so-called dark side. While at first this may appear to oppose the negation of sadness, and perhaps more so in cases of clinical depression, research has shown that there are valid reasons why sad songs are chosen.

Firstly, in playing sad music, one finds a connectivity between the song and mood. This connectivity helps to identify the feelings to assist what some researchers are calling a cognitive reappraisal of one's emotions (Van den Tol & Edwards , 2011). This is something I can attest to myself. In both listening to and composing music, on reflection, I did tend to draw an association between the music and what was happening in my life.

Secondly, the cognitive reappraisal is further utilised in the message that is conveyed in the song itself. This can be initially stimulated through the tone of the music; however, the lyrical message can affirm to the listener exactly what his/her issue is and the effect it has on him/her.

Thirdly, the use of music has been described as helpful in enabling clients suffering from depression to express emotions that would otherwise be curtailed (Eckhardt & Dinsmore, 2012). To this end, it was discovered that sad music was the most effective. It was held that uplifting music was not aligned to the emotional state of depressed clients, whereas sombre tones were more identifiable to their moods (Punkanen, Eerola,. & Erkkila, 2011).

This can best be illustrated through a personal anecdote. During my periods of depression, I would often listen to what may be described as "dark music," that is to say, music that is far from enlightening in its construct. One particular album that stands out from this time is Alice in Chains' *Dirt*. This album is a collection of dirges that remains an outstanding collection of such songs, from an era, the early 1990s, that had many such tracks.

I began to notice, during the art therapy sessions, that certain tracks were highly influential on my moods. One, the title track "Dirt," was particularly potent with lyrics such as "One that doesn't care; is one that shouldn't be," and "I want you to kill me, and dig me under; I want to live no more," all played to a slow grungy dirge.

Needless to say, this kind of music *was* influential on me, but not in a positive manner. Yet tracks like that were more or less on rotation as I became more immersed in the darkness that developed into depression.

Perhaps a description of the issues facing me at the time is warranted here. My partner of twenty-eight years was suffering from the insidious illness that is dementia. This illness takes the person whom you once knew and transforms her into a being that is alien to her prior self. Behavioural abnormalities together with cognitive incapacity result in an alienation of sorts in that she no longer recognised those around them, or for that matter her surroundings.

As a result, my partner eventually became confined to a hospice while the illness increased its hold and took away her remaining faculties. While it is true, in the context of things, she was alive, being unaware of one's surroundings is not what could be considered as having any quality of life.

In this context, I experienced a flux of emotions that crossed a multitude of streams, yet despite this plethora of emotions, one constantly returned, becoming in time the dominant stream: intense sadness. This was to become the prevailing emotion from this time on. I became reclusive, venturing out only to work. Even there, I was less than sociable. However, in the context of an automotive workshop, this was taken to be par for the course as the frustration of working on hot vehicles in confined spaces often led to angst.

Although I was unable to see it, I was deteriorating mentally, and perhaps physically as well. When the social worker who had been responsible for my partner during her hospitalisation asked me to make an appointment to see her, I agreed, assuming it was to discuss further details relating to the now rapidly deteriorating situation my partner found herself in. Curiously, after the preliminaries were dealt with, I was instead asked about my health. This took me aback since I presumed that any situation outside of the clinical supervision of the patient was not their responsibility, and as such, not something of a concern.

Initially, I was not forthcoming and tended to be recalcitrant and withdrawn, answering questions in short, measured sentences, determined not to give any more information than I thought absolutely necessary. There was a follow-up session in which it was discussed that, as I was involved in the situation, I was entitled to counselling, should I desire.

In such a situation, a person without inhibitions or suspicions as to the motive behind the offer would engage positively; this, however, was not how I chose to behave. I was concerned as to the purpose of the proposal and suspected it was some kind of plot to entrap me—how, I did not now know. Further sessions were organised that I attended since they got me away from work and, since they were medically-based, enabled me to be paid. I attended on the basis of gaining a respite from work that I disliked without losing pay.

Thus, an interesting scenario developed in which the social worker endeavoured to get a recalcitrant client to engage with the sessions and open up regarding the issues I was facing. Midway through one session, I was asked what interests I had that did not relate to work. I mentioned that I used to like taking photographs, but I had found it difficult to regain the desire to do so. It was suggested that I should find something of interest and take some photographs, using as much creativity as I could. I was to bring the results to the next meeting.

I did this and took snapshots from around the Burnett River, using the bridge architecture as framing. The shots were what my camera club buddies from Ballarat would have called record shots—that is, they were not spectacular but were framed well enough to satisfy the task. I did, as instructed, produce the shots at the next meeting. The reception was possibly one that was expected of a trained professional—supportive enough to maintain a glimmer of positivity while not deceiving me that a career was to be had in this field. Little did I know that I had entered the realms of art therapy.

A semblance of trust had now developed. I was asked whether there were any other recreational pursuits I enjoyed. I was tempted to say cricket, but I was at an age where playing cricket was well and truly out of the question. In passing, I mentioned that I had some instruments at home. This was somewhat of an understatement since my musical menagerie consisted of a twelve-string acoustic, six-string electric, and a bass guitar that I had, at one stage, been trying to learn. In addition, I had a drum kit that had not been used for some time.

As an aside, I said that years ago, while playing in a band, I used to write my own songs. The social worker said that since I had the means, why not try and write again, this time, using the feelings I was experiencing as the basis for the content. At first, I did not succeed in this, partly due to the rawness of the situation. Nevertheless, I kept going until I had written a song based on my feelings. Admittedly, I did borrow part of the melody from another artist, but as I never intended to perform or record the song, I decided not to worry too much about that.

At the next meeting, the song became the point of discussion. Using sections of the lyrics, the social worker was able to draw information out of me that would not have been forthcoming otherwise. The structure of the sessions had now changed from her doing the talking, with me largely belligerent and silent, to me now engaging more amenably.

The manner in which the construct of these sessions had begun to use the arts, and particularly music, is in line with professional thinking in instances where one needs to reach recalcitrant clients, and/or those who have difficulty expressing themselves (Gladding, 2010). The use of music, and in particular, sad music, has been shown to act as a catalyst that enables the client to engage with the counsellor and, thereby, develop a positive relationship (Bodner, Iancu, Gilboa, et. al. 2007).

The art therapy had, over time, worked. Where regular question and answer sessions had failed to achieve any results, changing to a program based largely on music and lyrics had broken down the barrier and brought about a change of attitude. I developed a more positive outlook on life in general. This is not to say I was completely over my depression, but it was no longer a dominant part of my life.

I began to engage somewhat with my workmates, and I made plans to visit family over Christmas—activities I had little interest in before the art therapy program. I continued to write songs and perform them at home. To expand further on my newfound enthusiasm, I decided to return to drumming, something I had not done since 1985. I set my drums up in the living room, and at times, I played until very late at night. Fortuitously, I lived on an acreage; this behaviour would not have been tolerated in a built-up area.

During the period of art therapy, my partner finally succumbed to her illness. Whilst I felt a sadness in her passing, I also felt some relief. She had suffered this illness for some years, and unbeknown to me, so had I. Nevertheless, I continued to write songs. I was determined not to become depressed again.

I had by this time begun to read academic texts. I had always had an interest in political writings, particularly those of a "left" persuasion. I remembered how I enjoyed the humanities and social sciences at school and became immersed in these subjects, devouring books on Karl Marx, Max Weber, and other sociologists, while my workmates instead read car and girlie magazines.

Reading these introductory texts, I considered the possibility of using this interest to instigate a career change. This would involve tertiary study and would require strict time management. Nevertheless, the more thought I gave to this, the more I believed university study to be an option I could pursue. I had, by this time, developed a skin condition that flared whenever I came into contact with certain chemicals at work. Equally important, I had also lost the desire to continue in my current field, believing I had gone as far as I could.

Ironically, an advertisement was broadcast for an information session at the local campus of the university. I decided to attend in order to find out what programs were on offer and whether they were applicable to the direction I saw my life going. To be succinct, this led to me completing an entry preparatory program, and four years later, graduating with a double degree as a Bachelor of Arts/Laws.

Tertiary study changed my life in ways that were not restricted to education. Before becoming a full-time student, I was unable to make use of campus facilities after hours. However, I was able to find a place, an oasis of sorts, where I could study, unwind, and interact. It was at this café that I met my future wife.

After some time, I discovered she had ambitions of becoming a teacher. Learning this, I encouraged her also to attend university. She graduated with a Bachelor of Learning Management (distinction) at the same ceremony as I. To my knowledge, we are the first husband and wife team to graduate at the same ceremony at this campus. I also encouraged my sister to obtain her Bachelor of Accounting at the same university. This enabled her to leave a job in which her health was suffering and pursue a career in accounting.

Much has been said about the so-called "butterfly effect," in which sometimes one action, regardless of how small, can effect great change. In reflection, I can see how the lives of at least three people, and possibly more, have been changed through my undertaking art therapy.

I am not endeavouring to indulge in grandiose statements, nor am I claiming to be the sole reason for the transition of these people; rather, I am stating that without the opportunity to express myself via the creative arts, things may have turned out quite differently.

References

Bodner, E. Iancu, I. Gilboa, A. Sarel, A. Mazor, A. & Amir, D. (2007). Finding words for emotions: The reactions of patients with major depressive disorder towards various musical excerpts, *The Arts in Psychotherapy*, vol. 34.

Congreve, W. (1757). *The mourning bride. A tragedy*. Dublin: Printed for Peter Wilson.

Eckhardt, K. J. & Dinsmore, J. A. (2012). Mindful music listening as a potential treatment for depression, *Journal of Creativity in Mental Health*, vol. 7.

Gladding, S.T. 2010, *The Creative Arts in Counselling*, Alexandria, VA: American Counselling Association

Punkanen, M. Eerola, T. & Erkkila, J. (2011)."Biased emotional recognition in depression: Perception of emotions in music by depressed patients," *Journal of Affective Disorders*, vol. 130.

Van den Tol, A. & Edwards, J. (2011). "A rationale for sad music listening after adverse emotional effects," *Psychology of Music*, vol. 41, no. 4.

Yun, S.H. & Gallant, W. 2010, "Evidence based clinical practice: The effectiveness of music-based intervention for women experiencing forgiveness/grief issues." *Journal of Evidence-Based Social Work*, vol. 7.

Chapter 7 -
Cantare e Suonare è una Salvezza per l'Essere Umano
By Mauro Lopizzo

Cantare e suonare è una salvezza per l'essere umano.

Nell'antica Grecia all'età di 11 anni ogni bambino suonava perfettamente due o tre strumenti. Oggi siamo fortunati se un bambino su dieci suona un solo strumento...Che cosa è successo? È possibile che i greci avessero tanto più talento di noi? Un tempo suonare uno strumento era del tutto naturale dato che la musica aveva un ruolo fondamentale nella vita quotidiana. Era un mezzo espressivo già a partire dai riti tribali ,fino a diventare una vera e propria arte,uno scrigno ricco di emozioni.Tutt'oggi le melodie hanno un forte impatto sulla nostra psiche, ma raramente riusciamo a beneficiarne appieno, limitandoci al solo ascolto. Le ragioni per cui una persona non impara a suonare possono essere molteplici. Fin da piccoli ci dicono che solo chi ha talento può diventare un buon musicista. Diamo per scontato che per poter imparare a suonare sia indispensabile essere intonati, avere buon orecchio e buon senso del ritmo. Così magari tanti di noi non ci provano nemmeno. Oppure,cominciamo a studiare, ma la complicatissima teoria e le difficoltà tecniche presto ci scoraggiano...Perché,se prima era tutto così facile,ora è tutto incredibilmente complicato? Che cosa è cambiato?In realtà non si tratta tanto del cosa, ma del come. Oggi l'insegnamento si basa sulle note, mentre i greci insegnavano le relazioni tra le note. Questa differenza, a prima vista poco significante, semplificava notevolmente lo studio della materiae permetteva di concentrarsi sulla vera abilità artistica: la comunicazione. Come disse il filosofo ateniese, Platone:

"La musica fa bene al cuore e all'anima."ha un effetto magnifico su di noi. ...

E' capace di sollevare l'anima verso la felicità

Personalmente ho iniziato a improvvisarmi batterista all'età di 5 anni, assemblando cartoni e pentole di diverse misure da formare una batteria molto singolare.Da allora è iniziata la mia vita musicale .... Devo dire che grazie a questa mia passione in qualsiasi momento di vita mi è servito come passepartout per le relazioni nella comunità.Ho coltivato anche la passione del canto e per me cantare significa esprimere se stessi, un equilibrio costante tra emozione e tecnica. "Canta che ti passa" recita il detto. È proprio vero perché sia la musica sia il canto sono dei potenti antistress. Cantare quindi fa bene alla salute e alla psiche: aumenta la funzionalità del sistema immunitario, favorisce il rilascio di ormoni e di serotonina, fa diminuire il livello di cortisolo (un ormone la cui produzione aumenta in condizioni di stress), riduce le tensioni muscolari, implica una respirazione più regolare e profonda tanto da aumentare l'ossigenazione nel sangue e migliorare la funzionalità cardiaca, favorisce la dilatazione dei vasi sanguigni come quando si ride o si assumono farmaci specifici. La musica e di conseguenza i suoni sono un messaggio universale da tutti compreso e con effetto immediato a livello psicofisico. D'altra parte uno tra i primi sensi utilizzati dal feto è proprio l'udito: quando il piccolo ascolta la voce della mamma e impara a distinguerla dalle altre, sa anche riconoscere le varie intonazioni a seconda delle emozioni che la madre sta vivendo.Cantare aiuta a rilassarsi e a buttare fuori le sensazioni e le emozioni negative vissute durante la giornata. Ciò vale in modo particolare per tutti coloro che non si occupano di musica per lavoro. Quindi anche solo canticchiare una canzone mentre si passeggia o si torna a casa oppure cantare sotto la doccia sono tutte azioni che migliorano l'umore, allontanano la stanchezza, fanno iniziare o terminare in modo positivo una giornata. In particolare sono molte le persone che cantano sotto la doccia o anche in macchina quando sono sole. L'effetto è benefico e liberatorio perchè la persona è sola e sente di poter dare libero sfogo alla sua energia, può cantare ciò che vuole senza timore di essere giudicata o criticata o presa in giro, assecondando anche lo stato d'animo del momento e quindi scegliendo la musica più adatta al suo umore.Comunque prevale il piacere di essere ascoltati e guardati dagli altri anche se le doti canore possono lasciare a desiderare.D'altra parte cantare insieme ad altre persone, come ad esempio in un coro, aumenta la sicurezza in se stessi, fa sentire parte di un gruppo coeso e migliora l'umore. Infatti il coro è tradizionalmente usato in tutto il mondo durante i riti di moltissime religioni per i suoi effetti rilassanti, energizzanti e coinvolgenti. Molte ricerche hanno evidenziato come nelle persone che cantano in coro aumenti la percezione di benessere e allo stesso tempo si viva la presenza degli altri come uno stimolo ad impegnarsi con regolarità. Alcune malattie senili, come la demenza, possono essere affrontate dai pazienti, partecipando ad un coro, così da mantenere la mente sempre in esercizio grazie alla necessità di ricordare le parole e la musica dei brani. Inoltre, presupposto fondamentale di chi canta in coro non è emergere, ma piuttosto amalgamare la propria voce con quella degli altri così da creare un insieme armonico equilibrato e omogeneo. Quindi, a meno che non ci sia qualche voce solista che deve emergere in alcuni casi prestabiliti, nel coro non bisogna cercare di mettersi in evidenza, evitando quindi situazioni di rivalità o narcisismo.Nella ricerca, gli scienziati si sono occupati di studiare come il canto, che di fatto è una forma di respirazione guidata, coinvolga la variabilità del battito cardiaco (HRV) e l'aritmia respiratoria sinusale (RSA), una variazione naturale del battito che avviene durante un ciclo di respirazione: l'accoppiamento di questi fattori infatti, oltre a provocare biologicamente un effetto calmante, favorisce le funzioni dell'apparato cardiovascolare. Per concludere...esorto tutti a intrapendere questa magica terapia che è il canto o imparare a suonare uno strumento.....io finchè il Signore mi darà la possibilità di farlo canterò e suonerò sempre.

Singing and Playing are a Salvation for the Human Being
by Mauro Lopizzo
(English Translation)

In ancient Greece, at the age of eleven, every child played perfectly two or three instruments. Today, we are lucky if one in ten children plays one instrument.... What happened? Is it possible that the Greeks had so much more talent than us? Once upon a time, playing an instrument was natural since music had an important role in everyday life. It was a means of expression.

As early in history as the tribal rituals, music was considered the most important thing humans had. Still today, melodies have a strong impact on our psyche, but we rarely manage to benefit from music fully, limiting ourselves to just listening. The reasons why a person does not learn to play can be explained if we consider that since childhood we are told that only those with talent can become good musicians. We assume that in order to learn to play, it is essential to be in tune, to have good ear, and a good sense of rhythm. Because of this ideology, many of us do not even try. Or we begin to investigate, but the complex theory and early technical difficulties discourage us.... Why, if before it was all so easy, it is now incredibly complicated? What has changed?

Today, teaching is based on the notes, while the Greeks taught the relationship between the notes. This difference, at first glance meaningless, serve to hide away the fact that the principle mechanism of music is communication of a different kind: emotional and spiritual. As Plato once said: "Music is good for the heart and soul." It has a great effect on us and is "capable of lifting the soul to happiness."

Personally, I started to improvise on drums at the age of five, assembling boxes and pots of different sizes to form a very rudimental drum kit. It was then that my musical journey began. Even just humming a song as you walk, or singing in the shower are all activities that improve mood.

The effect is beneficial and liberating because the person is alone and feels he can give free rein to his energy, can sing what he wants without fear of being judged or criticized or teased, favouring also the state of mind of the moment and then choosing the most suitable mood.

Some age-related diseases, such as dementia, can be addressed by patients participating in a choir, so as to keep their minds operational. I urge everyone to sing or play an instrument; it is magical therapy. Till God gives me a chance to sing and play, I will do it.

Chapter 8 -
My Favourite Coffee Shop
by Alfredo Zotti

Coffee shops of Europe, particularly in France and Italy, were meeting places where artists, poets, scientists, inventors, performing artists, and musicians often met to spend some time together and have a good chat about life, art, and the human condition.

In this age when computers, mobile phones, and iPads, or tablets, prevent us from socializing, given that socialization often happens in cyberspace, I am fortunate to say that I can still go to my favourite coffee shop where I meet many artists, musicians, and creative people.

I spend some time, every week, at my favourite coffee shop to talk to very interesting people. It is there that I have met not only many musicians and artists but also players and those who like to discuss politics. Contrary to what we are told—that we should never discuss politics—I think it is extremely important to be informed about politics and to discuss them with people who are able to embrace different perspectives, not just their own. It is always a pleasure to discuss things. I feel that artists must be concerned with what is happening around them to express their creativity fully.

Why this is good for me is not easy to explain in a few words but, basically, I believe that an artist needs to communicate with people in order to understand people's concerns, fears, hopes, and so on. It is very easy to become self-absorbed in one's own world, or universe, and to come to believe that the world works just as we think it does, that we have all of the answers. When one begins to talk to different people, one begins to understand that life is much more intricate than we give it credit for.

Being able to go to a coffee shop where creative people go, especially visual artists and musicians, is very inspiring and gives me courage to go on and explore the creative world, a world that is always expanding in terms of ideas.

Because of the people I met there, a very good idea came to my mind: to raise money for my local hospital by forming a band and playing in various venues to help disadvantaged people. This dream of mine has today come true, and I believe it helps me to become a more creative artist.

To this day, we have played at various fundraisers where my band and I have been able to make good money for our local hospital, Gosford Hospital of the Central Coast of New South Wales. We have raised thousands of dollars to help a variety of people, including homeless people, single mums, and so on.

I continue to organize fundraisers and, while it is not at all easy, I am learning to work in cooperation with people. I am a full-time caregiver for my wife, who has a number of disabilities, which means that I am already quite busy taking care of things at home; but I also have numerous interests, including writing, and playing, recording, and composing music, practicing visual art, and so on; I also help many people with mental disorders and disabilities online. Adding to this, sometimes to organize fundraisers is very challenging, to say the least, but also very rewarding. Indeed it is at fundraiser events that I have met many good people and fellow artists. These people also support me in what I do and, in particular, to ensure that I have fairly successful fundraisers. The friendship I have with these people is very helpful to me, particularly in terms of learning how to socialize well, something I was never good at.

Most recently, we have lost a dear friend who died due to unknown causes. He had a few health issues and was on a disability pension. Listening to music was a way for him to cope with his many problems. He was a great supporter of local artists both in Sydney and in the area, and many band members will tell you that he used to travel long distances to listen to his favourite bands. He also bought their CDs and was a great supporter of the local music industry and musicians.

It is events like the death of a good friend that bring people together. But more importantly, I have learned something really special by going to this coffee shop—that everyone, every single individual, has problems, and we are all in need of some art therapy. There is not one person whom I feel could not benefit from being involved in the arts in whatever way. Art therapy is good to all human beings, not only those who have a disability, but also to reasonably healthy people. We all have problems since life is full of challenges and obstacles that need to be overcome. With a bit of art therapy, the journey is much easier and we give our brain a chance to reenergize.

Just like Van Gogh and Toulouse Lautrec, I go to my coffee shop to enjoy my coffee, learn about people and life, and be in the company of creative friends. This is also part of my art therapy. I embrace life, no matter what problems I have, and I always create in my mind La Dolce Vita. I live a good life, interesting and full of emotions, feelings, and love as I learn to be a better human being.

Chapter 9 -
My Friend Colin Sydee
By Alfredo Zotti

I met Colin Sydee about three years ago, at Bremen Patisserie, a popular coffee shop situated in Umina, on the Central Coast of New South Wales. Ron Bruns is the owner of Bremen Patisserie, but he is also a music lover of rock and blues. For this reason, but also because of the wonderful roasted coffee that he serves, many musicians and artists go there. Colin was very passionate about music, particularly blues, and used to support local bands and artists, mostly by attending their gigs and buying their CDs. It was not uncommon for Colin to greet me by saying, "The Arc Riders are on this weekend, on Saturday, at Budgewoi. Are you coming?"

Colin simply loved music, and he told me that he strongly believed that music was one of the few good things about human beings. Music was what kept him motivated, what kept him hopeful for the future. He had survived a very serious truck accident that had caused some spinal injuries. Colin could walk and do most things, but he was in constant pain, having problems sitting down or simply walking. For this, he was given a disability pension and some compensation.

For many years, Colin wanted to buy his own little house, and he finally did just a few months before his death, which is the saddest part for me. He loved his little house, built on the grounds of a Caravan Park in Empire Bay on the Central Coast of New South Wales, Australia. He had a little garden, and the little place looked fantastic—just right for a single person. And while Colin lived alone, he had hundreds of friends.

It was not uncommon to see Colin in a photograph with famous entertainers like the popular Australian rocker Kevin Borich or the famous singer Delta Goodrem. He supported most Australian artists, and he had an extensive collection of thousands of CDs that he was to catalogue, with the help of a friend, but never got around to it.

As it often happens, Colin also developed some psychological problems due to his truck accident, including some anxiety and depression. For this reason, we developed a strong friendship within a few months because I am a helper for many people who struggle with anxiety and, as it is widely known, all people can develop anxiety at any time, particularly after a traumatic life event such as a car accident. It is called Post Traumatic Stress Disorder (PTSD).

It was Colin who suggested, about three years ago, that I should organize a fundraiser and play music with my band, the then Future 4 Band, so I could not only have fun playing music, but I could also help disadvantaged people who happen to go to the hospital to ask for help, such as homeless people and single mums who often develop post-natal depression. It was a terrific idea, and when I spoke to the band members, they agreed to do it.

Over the past three years, we have organized many fundraiser for our local hospital, Gosford Hospital, and we have raised thousands of dollars. We continue to do so.

Colin was always there to help with ideas and support for the fundraisers, and he always said that they were great causes. He liked me as a pianist and told me that I should play with more than one singer—that I should play with as many musicians as possible. I have certainly tried to do that. At the next fundraiser, which takes place in a couple of months, we are going to honour the memory of Colin Sydee, a good friend of most musicians on the Central Coast and in the Sydney area. His support for musicians is well known by Toni Cini, the lead singer of the Arc Riders, who said that it will not be easy to forget Colin, a rare man who would travel long distances to listen to his favourite band play his music.

We probably never realized, while he was alive, how important Colin was in the music scene because he kept music alive simply by discussing it every day. He made the musicians feel important, and he always encouraged people to get together and play music. Music was his life, even though he did not play an instrument. A funny but sad thing is that I started to teach Colin piano a couple of months before his unexpected death. At almost sixty years of age, Colin learned piano with ease. I discovered that he had perfect pitch and he had absolutely no trouble playing chords. So fast was his ability to learn the piano that he would have been able to play piano boogie in a very short time, something I had never seen before in any student.

I teach the piano as a volunteer to children with autism and Asperger's who cannot afford piano lessons. I only have a few students at present. Colin was one of the best in terms of learning new things.

Colin had numerous talents, including the ability to distinguish Australian birds by their Latin and common names, and he also knew a lot about plants, particularly native Australian plants.

It will be very difficult to forget Colin. I think his memory will live with me for many years to come, if not for life. Every day, I will think of Colin, my friend who encouraged me to play with as many people as possible and who loved music. There is not one musician I know who does not respect Colin, who had an encyclopaedic knowledge of Australian blues bands and musicians. Blues was his religion, as he said.

Many musicians, on the Central Coast, remember Colin, such as Bruce Johnson, guitarist of Rivershak and music director of Xabc, who organizes many concerts with local and overseas artists. At Colin's funeral, Bruce mentioned the many messages that Colin sent him on Facebook. Colin simply loved to talk music.

I decided to include this short piece of writing about Colin, in this book, for two important reasons: one is because he always felt that music was a great therapy and that all people should listen to music or play an instrument. "Music is life," he would say; and secondly, because by writing a little about him, in this book, I can immortalize his memory. Colin was a simple man who loved music and lived a simple life. He was not perfect and struggled with his spinal injury. But he always told me that music was his life—that it made him happy to be alive and able to celebrate many friendships. He told me that I was a terrific musician and a good artist, and I believe him, and because of that, I am becoming a better musician and artist every day. Colin was a simple man, but in my mind, a working class hero who made a difference in my world.

Chapter 10 -
Connecting with Art:
My Experience with Homeless Youths
by Samuel Mann

Writing about my own art experience was something I had been contemplating for a while before Alfredo eventually popped the question. In asking me if I would be interested in the idea, the word "competition" somehow came up, and I thought to myself, *If art is about anything, it is certainly not about competing with anyone.* The word immediately rang a bell inside my head. Competition is stressful, good for athletes and the neurotypical, but not for people who are on the autism spectrum disorder. I am not officially diagnosed with Asperger's, but one of my daughters is, and we are very much alike. Looking back at my past, it became clear to me why I failed to get right so many normal things. For example, why I always did poorly in exams and interviews, why I was always quiet among people, why I became so easily obsessed, and so on. I, therefore, decided I was going to write about my experience at a shelter for homeless youths, many of whom were not much different from me and were victims of various emotional and traumatic disturbances.

One of my first discoveries trying to attract homeless youths to art was their reaction when I posed the question: Could I encourage you to spend a little time in doing some art? "No" would be the swift rebound from most of them. "I don't know how to draw." As if anyone had said anything about knowing how to draw. They only saw what was before their eyes. Far be it that art is about whether or not you're an artist. The famous French artist and sculptor, Edgar Degas (1961), is quoted as saying, "Painting is easy when you don't know how, but very difficult when you do." We're all artists in our own way. Some of us know it. Some of us don't. Art, contrary to what we are accustomed to thinking, is not just the visual outcome of a masterpiece on canvas. It is firstly a process that most people never think about that occurs in the mind long before it materializes on any kind of surface.

I was often criticized for intimidating my young clients with my art. But was I? As an artist, I never imagined that I would unintentionally drive people away from me. I like to think that I am good at what I am doing, but not so good as to be scary. It is true that a beautiful woman can be intimidating for some people, but I never thought of my art in that respect. After all, art is just another way of expressing ourselves and communicating with others, sharing what's hidden inside us. We do it all the time when we articulate, through the way we move, our touch, the look in our eyes when we're in love, and the innocent smile we give as babies.

No, I wasn't asking the youths to be like me. That would be copying. They would have to be a camera to do that. Of course, I'm aware that photography is an art too, and I had made the mistake once of erroneously conveying that I didn't consider it to be. But there's a difference between the camera and an artist. As a portraitist, it is not unusual for one to encounter that difference sometimes. A good example is from the movie, *The World of Suzie Wong* (2004), in which William Holden played Robert Lomax, the leading character and a portrait artist. After finishing his painting of Suzie, a local Chinese prostitute played by Nancy Kwan, she looks at it and says to him:

Suzie: I like it very much, but not look like me.

Robert: It's what I think you look like. That's the difference between an artist and a camera. An artist always tries to look deeper.

The camera is mechanical, whereas the artist is not. One reproduces what is seen; the other, what we do not see. The artist always draws or paint what he or she sees and not what everyone sees. Philosophically, let's put it this way. There are several ways of looking at someone: what the person actually is (a fact, for example), what the person thinks he or she is, what the artist sees, the person's interpretation of what the artist sees, what a third person thinks the person is, what the artist sees, and so on and so on. Nevertheless, with a lot of practice and training, an artist is, in most instances, able to capture something that is strikingly familiar of the person he or she is working on. There was a particular case I recall of a girl in the shelter painting a full-size figure of someone on canvas. Just then, my supervisor, a woman, came in because it was time for dinner, and everyone had to vacate the room. She stared at the painting for a moment, and while she was on her way out, I heard her quietly remark to herself that it looked just like the artist, who incidentally had a curvaceous body. Naturally, I couldn't help smiling and replied that it was what all artists did. We reflect ourselves in our work, though not literally always, but metaphorically, so to speak.

And so it was that I began to formulate in my mind my own understanding of art in a way that others could relate to. To do so, I began to focus on art more as a process and experience. As a process evolving in our minds, I believe we could all find a common ground with it since it doesn't have to turn out to be a Picasso or Raphael painting. As an experience, we can all enjoy it and learn from it. That way, it can help to heal wounds for some of us, shed more light on our feelings, make us progress personally as human beings, and solve problems in the real world by stretching our intuition and creativity. One of the things Albert Einstein said that made me think of him more as an artist than as a scientist was:

"Imagination is more important than knowledge. For knowledge is limited to all we now know and understand, while imagination embraces the entire world, and all there ever will be to know and understand." (Nilsson, 2010)

It is so sad, therefore, when budgetary cuts are to be made that arts and the social sectors are the ones to suffer first and the most. Humanity always takes second place before corporate enrichment in our "real" world.

When I first started out as an arts programmer, I had great ideas about holding workshops and passing on my experience as an artist to kids, getting them excited about poetry, singing, and playing a musical instrument. While I must admit that music is not my strong point, I have tried for many years to learn how to sing and play the guitar, so I do know a bit about it and can recognize a talented singer or musician when I see one. In fact, I was fortunate to witness some very talented youths who came along but were ruining their lives with drugs and caving under peer pressure. Besides, my role was not that of a typical teacher, but more of a facilitator and coach. This meant that I didn't have to prove how good an artist I was to my youthful followers. To illustrate my point, we had a youth who was writing a story and making a lot of grammatical and spelling errors. One day, the education instructor, a bright attractive young girl and a trained teacher by profession, and I were having a conversation about this youth. From a teacher's perspective, she felt that the youth needed to get his grammar and spelling in order and that he would have to devote some time learning how to write properly. In his defence, I told her that, as an artist, my approach would be to encourage the youth to write as much as possible and leave the learning for later. Any attempt to make him sit down and struggle with English grammar and spelling would unleash red flags in the air and discourage him from proceeding further. Clearly, he was in no condition to accept the challenge of traditional teaching methods since he was one of those kids we observed to have mental issues. I think we both agreed in the end, and happily so, that the way forward for the youth was to continue freely expressing his thoughts.

I was particularly touched by one girl who was said to be schizophrenic. She never did any kind of art, but she would come into the art room and quietly sit down for a while. When I approached her, she replied that all she wanted was to enjoy the atmosphere. I realized then how similar an art gallery or any place where art is produced, for that matter, was to a church. I myself soon began to enjoy the presence of the paintings and drawings that surrounded me. When the stretched canvases ran out, I got this weird idea of using the disposed head frames of beds that were stored in the art room; we wrapped them and placed them on the easel. Just looking at the blank canvas on the easel would be sufficient to motivate me to think of something to paint. I noticed it had the same effect on some of the youths.

At one time, there was a guy, an extremely talented artist, who had gotten discharged before for losing his temper and attacking one of the staff, but he came back after many months had passed. He hardly ever spoke to me or anyone previously, but on this occasion, he had undergone a complete changeover and was on his best behaviour towards everyone. Besides lecturing to me about his comprehensive knowledge of art, why he didn't believe it made sense hiding to do graffiti, and his use of sacred geometry and spiritualism in his work, he showed me something that I never knew about and for which I am thankful to him. In one of the pieces he was working on, he added glitters to the paint so that when the light struck it in a certain angle, you could see some areas of it twinkling. I thought it was quite an inter-active technique, and I found it came in handy when I was doing a painting of an eye as a farewell gift for a staff member.

Singing was a favourite among some of the girls. There were five girls who had tremendous potential. One of them suffered from depression and had made a few attempts on her own life, but what a fantastic voice she had. I was simply stunned when she did a cover of Bonnie Tyler's "Turn Around." Another had told me she wanted to become a rock star and had composed her own songs. One afternoon, she suddenly came out of her shell and started performing a song of hers. Not only could she sing, but she was also a good dancer who had studied a bit of ballet. Another girl who was autistic sang with an angelic voice and accompanied herself well on the guitar. My favourite, however, was one who had a voice like Adele. Her rendition of "Someone Like You" was really professional. She had perfect timing, control, and pitch. The fifth girl was not as impressive as the others, but was determined, and with the right coaching, I had reason to believe she would eventually blossom.

Much as I tried to sell the idea of art being a process, the youths just weren't buying it, or they were not yet ready to abandon their fixed mindsets. Overall, I had to come to terms with the reality that art was just another option they had, and many others were available to them within the establishment. I was also confronting a hit and miss situation where my potential clients were unpredictably coming and going. Those who really showed a strong interest were either gifted or liked doing art. The others were mostly into hip hop and sports. Doing traditional art is not what I was into or how I see the future of art unfolding. I am really more of a digital artist and would have liked to use computerized tools to create more excitement and liveliness, but this was not possible owing to security concerns.

Nevertheless, part of my strategy was to paint and sketch a few pictures that I thought the youths would connect with. For this purpose, I had to change my style and choose certain themes like love, happiness, hope, animals, fear, sadness, things that I believed they would be able to relate to. For instance, one of the pieces I did was a colourful psychedelic painting of Bob Marley and another was of a group of youths showing various facial expressions to reflect how they were feeling inside. Most of these paintings or drawings happen to be the kind that one would not normally hang on the walls of a private home. They are not decorative, so to speak. The intention is to entice the viewer to contemplate what they represent.

Fig. 10-1: Hope
Acrylics with charcoal and pastel on un-primed canvas. 29.5″ x 40.4″ (75 cm x 102.6 cm)
Message of faith to many of the homeless youths who felt trapped.

Fig. 10-2: Michael Jordan
Acrylics with charcoal and pastel on un-primed canvas. 30″ x 30″ (76 cm x 76 cm).
Appealing to the sports fans among the youths.

Fig. 10-3: Love

Acrylics with charcoal and pastel on canvas. 30″ x 30″ (76 cm x 76 cm).
What I felt many young boys dreamed about, including myself, when I was their age.

Fig. 10-4: Hip Hop

Charcoal and pastel on paper. 11″ x 13.5″ (28cm x 33.6 cm).
A scene from one of the frequent hip hop sessions.

Fig. 10-5 Guitar Player
Charcoal on paper. 11" x 13.5" (28cm x 33.6 cm).
Sketch of one of the musically talented youths working out.

Fig. 10-6: Picasso

Charcoal and pastel on canvas. 30″ x 30″ (76 cm x 76 cm).
My first demo to the youths.

Fig. 10-7: Horse and Man
Acrylics. 20″ x 40.4″ (51 cm x 102.6 cm).
An attempt to portray the connection between people with autism and animals

Fig. 10-8: Bob Marley
Acrylics. 29.5″ x 40.4″ (75 cm x 102.6 cm).
An experiment with colours and the love for music.

Fig. 10-9: Lost in Thought
Acrylics. 30″ x 30″ (76 cm x 76 cm).
Many homeless youths are in a typical situation where
they are confused and searching to find themselves.

Fig. 10-10: Homeless

Acrylics. 30″ x 30″ (76 cm x 76 cm).
The different expressions of fear, depression,
innocence, and resilience I saw among the homeless.

References

Gammell, R. H. I., & Degas, E. (1961). The shop-talk of Edgar Degas. Boston: University Press

Holden, W., Kwan, N., Quine, R., Stark, R., Patrick, J., Mason, R., Osborn, P., ... Paramount Pictures Corporation. (1989). The World of Suzie Wong. Hollywood, CA: Paramount Pictures.

Mason, R. (1957). *The world of Suzie Wong*. Cleveland: World Pub. Co.

Nilsson, B. J. (2010, March 20). Imagination Is More Important Than Knowledge Comments. Retrieved September 05, 2016, from http://www.saturdayeveningpost.com/2010/03/20/history/post-perspective/imagination-important-knowledge.html

Shea, P. (n.d.). The Role of National Association of State Mental Health Programs Directors in Promoting Trauma-Informed Mental Health Care. Retrieved September 5, 2016, from www.nasmhpd.org

.

Chapter 11 -
Poets of the Caribbean Circle (POTCar)

Poets of the Caribbean (POTCar) Circle is a group of writers—educators, artists, theologians, and business people—representing various countries of the Caribbean, namely Jamaica, Guyana, and Trinidad. Most of our poems speak on behalf of our indigenous as well as enslaved African, Asian, and European descendants. We are a people with a common history whose inhabitants have been oppressed by French and Spanish colonizers and later by Britain, who turned our Caribbean lands into sugar plantations. For centuries, the fight for emancipation and freedom raged before receiving independence from British rule during the 1960s. It is not surprising that our history of suffering and hardship emanates a fused legacy of cultures pulsating with colour, richness, and vibrancy within our work.

Our tone can be misunderstood because it is influenced by a remnant psychological anger generated from attempts by dominant cultures to trample on our dignity and self-worth. It is also tinged by a rebellion against present structures of oppression that have perpetuated inequities and injustice in various forms. On the other hand, we can laugh at ourselves, turning serious matters into something humorous.

As writers, we seek validation and an outlet to vent the anxieties and neuroses of the past that still haunt our present selves. We, therefore, use poetry and other art forms as a medium through which we can find redemption and as cathartic expressions of a people seeking to reconstruct, rediscover, and redefine ourselves as post-colonial people without denying the events that have shaped us.

Consequently, we are in the process of compiling our writings to develop an anthology of voices, distinctly Caribbean, undergirded by our history. These poetic expressions are based on our lived experiences along the continuum of existential issues, which affect us, as well as the rest of humanity.

You can find POTCar online at www.facebook.com/potcarcircle

Cynthia Pearson
Madam Chair (POTCar Circle)

Fig. 11-1: POTcar logo

If Only I Could Paint
by Alan Pena

Here I am,
sitting up in my room,
gazing out at the gloom
and thinking of you,
wishing you were here
to share this moment in time.
If only I could paint,
I would paint a picture for you,
on a canvas large,
with a palette and a brush.
I would stroke flowers of every hue,
Red, yellow, and blue,
purple too. In a green field
under a sky of blue,
I would paint buttercups and daisies,
poppies brightly red and black,
lavender and roses that you could almost smell;
there would be butterflies
floating on the breeze
brightly coloured above the flowers,
bluebells and dahlias next to honeysuckle roses,
hibiscus and iris and orchids too.
Busy bees hovering in the air,
happily feeding on nectar fresh.
If only I could paint
jasmine and jonquil and forget-me-nots,
sunflowers with their heads held high,
no wallflowers here but wisteria instead.
I would paint birds of paradise
high up in the sky
soaring overhead.
There would be no poplar trees bearing their strange fruit.
If only I could paint,
I would paint this picture for you.
But here I sit in my lonely room,
looking out at the gloom thinking of you,
wishing you were here to hold my hand
and share with me this moment in time.
If only I could paint!

Let Me Touch You There
by Alan Pena

I can feel your hurt,
I can feel your pain,
I can sense your melancholy state,
let me touch you there where melancholia resides,
let me reach you deep inside.
Let me touch you there.
Let me try to soothe the place where melancholia hides.
I can feel your sadness,
I can feel that lonely place,
deep within where melancholia hides.
Let me touch you there.
Let me bring you some light to brighten your dark insides,
to shine through the shadows of your mind.
Let me touch you there,
please let me try.
I can feel your need
I can feel your yearning too.
I can try to understand if you want me to,
so let me touch you there.
Let me come inside,
let me help to soothe your troubled mind,
let me touch you there and bring you hope,
let me touch you there with love;
please do not despair
let me touch you there.

Chapter 12 - Healing on the Run
by Ernest Dempsey

Harry Houdini is remembered as a great escape artist. People would put loads of chains on him, and he could get out of them, becoming free. This skill of his was entertaining to people. They loved seeing him escape to freedom. Hardly anyone doubts that Houdini's skill of escaping chains and confinement was actually art.

In the realm of psychology, do we consider escaping an art? Or is it a negative way of managing stress?

Growing up in a small town in Pakistan's northwest, I knew loneliness firsthand—a deep, inherent sense of being alone amidst people. Loneliness was my constant companion. Paradoxical, I know, to say so. At the same time, I took a fancy to the lively, adventurous, and inspiringly unconventional characters in TV shows from the West—my gate to the *other* world. Between my immediate reality of loneliness and stress and the remote *other* world, my mind created a new world—that of creative mental play.

Mine was a world where all these characters endlessly engaged in all cool things—picnics, banter, combat with the bad guys, games, and sports...you name it. Unlike the people around me, they didn't age or die or change by the real world's laws. I, like the most generous creator, made them immortal. And while they lived in a safe and exciting world, their creator had to live for a good while in the boring, routine, stressed world each day.

It didn't take my mental paradise long to take the form of writing. I started writing at age twelve. The more ethereal pleasures of imagination and memory started getting chronicled on paper. This marked the birth of my creative pride. But it took about a decade or so for me to face the word "escapism." I had probably known it all along, but I didn't pay it much heed—it hardly occurred to me that the real world, which has more of a claim on me than I had assumed all these years while foraying away from it, would be called a certain word.

The negative overtones of "escapism," as it was discussed in literature, particularly in the field of psychology, were quite obvious. It made me see a fugitive in the mirror every time I stood before it, following a session of mental play. And it was more so if I didn't materialize the mental play in written form. Pride has a dark side, and mine had started slowly gnawing at my self-esteem. Now I could see I wasn't just creating; I was on the run from a world that had ordained that being on the run was the main indication of a coward, a worthless person, and so on.

Yet in the darkest days and nights of my life, I had to be on the run. Every time the real world failed me, I had to escape—to make a quick leap into the realm of my immortal friends, who celebrated my presence without worrying whether I had enough money or a job or words of respect from people in the real world. To heal the wounds of the real, and thus get ready to keep going, I needed an escape into the virtual.

But is it bad? Is it something to watch with caution that I could go into the virtual, heal, and return to the real as a stronger and tenacious being? Isn't it an art, something to celebrate?

In my view, escape is a life-saving means—a tool, a resource, and a basic right to have an alternate, safe, and nurturing world where one can replenish one's existential energy. It is an art—a therapeutic art. I would learn many years later, with my introduction to the practice of guided imagery used as therapy, the value of mental play.

Houdini could escape chains and confinements. He was a fabulous artist. And so are all those lonely souls who have, over time, interiorized the art of escaping disturbing reality at the right time without burning all boats. Escapism is not a negative trait or habit; you just need to whet your command of its operation to make the most of its healing power.

Chapter 13 - Singing to Heal
by Judy Wright

When I was a small child, from the time I was less than four years old, it was evidently quite easy for me to learn songs from the radio and from recordings. This is something I was told and I don't have much memory of it, but I was often asked to "perform" at family gatherings. The times that I do remember seem rather devoid of feeling, probably because I survived my turbulent family life by shutting down. When I was four, my mother took me to a TV studio to audition for a children's amateur show and I was chosen as one of the participants. I sang "The Song from Moulin Rouge," rather odd for a 4-year-old to sing, but I was told it would be "cuter" than singing the more-common "How Much Is That Doggie in the Window?" This was in the early 1950s, by the way, so a lot of people today would not have even heard of the latter song.

As the years went by, I enjoyed singing at school and in church and in high school, immensely enjoyed participating in the choir. It was an all-girls school and we sang a lot of classical and sacred music. I would become so wrapped up in the music and work so hard at it that often times, right before a concert, I would totally lose my voice, which was extremely frustrating.

Looking back, I can see how singing has always been a means of both escape and emotional expression, which were badly needed when I was young. As an adult, I was able to participate in a couple of choirs for a few years, but then gave it up when employment and parenthood required most of my time.

Two years ago, I learned of a show choir that was looking for new members. Having been retired for a couple of years from an oppressive job situation, I was looking for some way to get back into music, so I auditioned and was accepted. For the first time, I am now also doing choreography and am finding it to be much more work than singing alone, but it's a good kind of work. Just going to practices and rehearsals can improve my mood if I'm having a bad day because it requires me to interact with other people, which I tend to avoid if I'm feeling depressed. It's the music itself, though, that can still allow me to transcend the day-to-day challenges that arise just through living my life and having a family. Perhaps it's a form a mindfulness which makes it helpful, but it certainly does keep me focused on the present moment. If I can lose myself in it enough, it can invoke memories, both visual and emotional, that can colour the present – almost like seeing things from a bigger perspective.

I don't know exactly how this works but singing does add another dimension to my life that feels unique to me in relation to my friends and family who don't share that same interest (or passion, I should probably say). I value being able to pursue my love of music and hope I'm still able to sing for quite a few more years before my voice ages too much!

Part III - Authors, Artists, and Other Contributors

Cynthia Pearson

Fig. 14-1: Portrait of Cynthia Pearson drawn by Alfredo Zotti with white and normal pencils

Although a Spanish teacher by profession, Cynthia sees herself as an educator interested in issues that affect teacher professional development. Outside of teaching, she is bookish, a lover of books, and her children call her a bookworm. Because her head is usually buried in a book, she considers herself an introvert. However, she is deeply intuitive with a creative mind. Unsurprisingly, she is a supporter of the arts and enjoys going to the theatre, listening to music, and appreciating good painting, slam poetry, photography, and the like, all of which help to enhance her appreciation of life.

Cynthia began to develop a more than passing interest in writing poetry from about grade two in primary school, but this interest became a fledgling skill that began while doing A-Level English Literature. As a university student in Jamaica in the mid '80s, she enrolled in a creative writing course. At the end of that course, she was pleased to have one of her poems published in the *Arts Review*, a volume dedicated to budding creative writers from the Faculty of Arts and General Studies. In 2013, she was officially named chair of the poetry group Poets of the Caribbean (POTCar) Circle, whose members are largely Caribbean nationals at home and in the diasporas.

The reader will discover that Cynthia's writing style is as varied as the issues that concern her.

Samuel Mann

Fig. 14-2: Drawing of Samuel Mann by Alfredo Zotti (2015)

Samuel Mann is a self-styled existentialist artist originally from Guyana who combines art with poetry and music to share with his audience the experiential joy of creativity. A former diplomat, lecturer, project manager, and reporter, Samuel began drawing at a very early age, but he abstained from art for many years after finishing his history undergraduate program at university and becoming a foreign service officer. While serving in Brussels as a government representative to the European Commission and the African, Caribbean, and Pacific Group of States, he developed a strong interest in international development and later went on to earn a Master's in the field. As an artist, Samuel is open and keen to exploring new ways of re-inventing and presenting art in a non-traditional format that is both aesthetic and alive. He is passionate that the future of art lies in its adaptation to science and the innovative use of digital technology to take it to the next level of surrealism. Samuel also belongs to the highly talented POTCar Circle (Poets of the Caribbean Circle), is married with two daughters, and currently resides in Canada.

Krystyna Laycraft

Fig. 14-3: Portrait by Alfredo Zotti special ink, pencils and other media, 2015

Krystyna was born in Poland. She holds a Master of Science in Theoretical Physics from the University of Warsaw and a PhD. in Education from the University of Calgary. After moving from Poland to Canada, Krystyna worked first as a physics instructor and later as a research scientist in the Department of Physics at the University of Calgary.

Later, she was involved in organizing senior high schools in Warsaw, Calgary, and Vancouver. For ten years, Krystyna was running and acting as a president of Equilibrium International Education Institute in Calgary.

During that time, she studied art by attending courses on Visual Art, Landscape Painting, Free Brush Technique, and workshops on mixed media.

Krystyna is the author of many articles and four books on emotions and psychological development: *Creativity as an Order through Emotions, Feeling Life, Journey through the Lands of Feelings,* and *The Courage to Decide.*

Currently, she offers assistance to troubled and gifted adolescents and young adults and helps them to achieve their potential. She also delivers seminars and workshops that include topics related to emotional needs and emotional development of adolescents, the role of creativity in their psychological development, and the process of decision making.

For more information on her work and teachings, visit: http://www.krystyna-laycraft.com and https://ucalgary.academia.edu/KrystynaLaycraft

Dr. Bob Rich

Fig. 14-4: Portrait of Bob Rich by Alfredo Zotti 2014. Pastels and pencils

Bob Rich is a professional grandfather. His main motivation is to transform society to create a sustainable world in which his grandchildren and their grandchildren in perpetuity can have a life, and a life worth living. This means reversing environmental idiocy, which is now threatening us with extinction, and replacing a culture of greed and conflict with one of compassion and cooperation.

So far, he has retired five times as a:

- Research scientist
- Builder's labourer
- Nurse
- Director of his professional association
- Counselling psychologist

Bob is still going strong as a storyteller, writer, and editor. To date, he has fifteen published books you can inspect at http://bobswriting.com (read the first chapter of each). Five of them won awards. He also does professional editing for a number of small, independent publishers and a steady stream of writers pre-submission.

Rather than a square peg in a round hole, he is a fractal-shaped peg that makes its own hole, so his writing doesn't fit into genres. His main aim is to entertain, but as with every other writer, his belief system underlies everything he writes. What is that?

Have a read of his essay https://bobrich18.wordpress.com/how-to-change-the-world/

Victor Paul Scerri

Fig. 14-5: Caricature of Victor Paul Scerri, who is a wonderful friend and a sport, by Alfredo Zotti (2015)

Born in London, Victor Paul Scerri grew up in a multicultural family, which was not easy back in the old days. Today, being from an ethnic background in England is fairly normal, but when he was a teenager and went to school, having a typical English mother, blonde with blue eyes, and a father with olive-coloured skin, from his Maltese-Italian ancestry meant he was not always accepted, and hence, he suffered much from being bullied at school.

Later, in his adult years, Victor married and divorced a Norwegian woman; he then moved to Japan with a Japanese partner, and later, to Madeira (third time lucky), an archipelago of Portugal. With such a background, it was inevitable for him to put pen to paper and become a writer.

Victor is a retired document control engineer and entrepreneur, and he received the Norwegian Cultural Award for his efforts in restoring a fourteenth-century wine cellar. He studied at the Medway College of Art, where he achieved second place in a prestigious, award-winning, oil painting competition in Great Britain.

His first works as a writer and artist were published by *Recovering the Self: A Journal of Hope and Healing*. In recognition of his art exhibits, one of his Zen paintings was chosen as the cover image for the April 2011 issue of the journal. He continues to publish articles at EzineArticles.com and has been an active team writer of short stories. He was chosen by the President of Porto Santo to narrate a video of the island back in March 2015; see:
https://www.youtube.com/watch?v=OyCX63qWrt8. His latest book/s is in progress. You can follow his work via http://nicewriters.com.

Debbie Bradley & Michael Bradley

Debbie Bradley is the mother of three and a grandmother of two. She is happily married and resides in sunny Central Queensland. She has held many roles in her life as a clerk, cleaner, sales rep, staff supervisor, cook, waitress, business owner, and after graduating with distinction as a mature student, she is now a teacher. She has won two scholarships, one of which allowed her to travel to India and teach rescued children. These experiences have all shaped her; however, the roles that have predominantly impacted her have been that of victim, artist, and, ultimately, survivor. As a teacher and as one who cares for the whole child, she knows that you cannot feed the mind when the heart and soul are hungry for happiness. She has personally experienced and believes wholeheartedly in the power of creativity and in its amazing ability to heal.

Michael Bradley has had many titles, and it is extremely difficult to sum him up in a short bio. He has been called husband, father, grandfather, brother, and friend by those who love him. His working hats have also been many, from a sailor specialising in marine engineering to a talented musician who can play almost any instrument he picks up, to a mechanic of twenty-five years, a role he had to abandon after developing a severe allergy to the harsh chemicals used in this career. Around the same time, he lost his first partner of twenty-eight years to Alzheimer's disease, and as a result, he was left emotionally bankrupt. Michael retreated into a world of music to survive the resulting overwhelming depression. Seeking a solution, he entered into university and graduated with a double degree in arts (majoring in sociology) and law. In the meantime, he met and later married Debbie, whom he also convinced to study. Michael is still studying and will complete an applied sociology degree, practical legal training, and a teaching degree in the coming year. Michael is a passionate activist for human rights and equality for women, and he has embraced a vegan lifestyle.

Paul Corcoran

Paul Corcoran is a clinical psychologist in private practice, a field he has worked in for over thirteen years. In his early working days, he had stints working in a surf shop, the banking industry, working as a builder's labourer, and doing a solid few years in the recruitment industry. Basically, he did anything that paid the bills as he worked his way through his university studies.

Paul is the father of two beautiful children who never cease to amaze him as they become increasingly independent little beings. He loves sports, both as a participant and as an observer, and he spends a good deal of his time on weekends watching his kids engage in their various sporting pursuits. He is known by his friends as having extremely diverse musical interests, ranging from classical music to hip hop to a few Taylor Swift gems, his exposure to which he blames entirely on his daughter.

Feeling it is a great privilege to do the work he does, Paul is never lost for new areas to explore in terms of professional development and the application of philosophical concepts to the more practical demands of therapy. He views the trust placed in him as a therapist as an incredible privilege and one he tries never to take lightly. He says watching people make meaningful changes in their lives is what keeps him going in his career.

Alan Pena

Alan Pena does not consider himself a poet, but he does enjoy writing. He is an ex-disc jockey and also worked for many years for an international organization based in Brussels, Belgium, where he lives.

Ernest Dempsey

Ernest Dempsey is a writer, editor, blogger, and journalist based in Orlando, Florida. He runs a popular blog *Word Matters!* at http://www.ernestdempsey.com/ and edits the journal *Recovering the Self* and its blog. Dempsey is a sceptic, vegetarian, and advocate for animal and human rights.

Judy Wright

Judy has been living with depression for many, many years. She has found various things that have helped her, including therapy and medication, but she also got involved with a show choir after she retired from the corporate world because singing makes her feel better and also has given Judy a broader network of friends.

Alfredo Zotti

Fig. 14-6: Musician, composer, and multi-talented visual artist Alfredo Zotti at the piano

Alfredo Zotti is the son of the late Luciano Zotti (https://it.wikipedia.org/wiki/Luciano_Zotti), Italian composer, orchestra conductor, and musical director, and his wife, Cristina Zotti.

Alfredo, his parents, and brother Giovanni migrated to Sydney, Australia in 1974. At first, life was difficult because the family worked in a wood factory for little money. As time went on, Luciano began to work as a musician and music teacher and life slowly improved for him and his family.

In 1981, after many traumatic events, Alfredo began his lifelong challenge of living with bipolar disorder. He quickly hit rock bottom, spending time as a homeless person and turning to street drugs and alcohol to medicate his symptoms. But life improved after hospitalization and careful outpatient monitoring.

Alfredo married Cheryl MacDonald, who also suffers with bipolar disorder, and he was able to enrol in a university course. He gained an honours degree in sociology and anthropology. He went on to study clinical psychology at the University of Newcastle, but he did not complete his degree because he felt that academia had taken the wrong path in the prevention and cure of mental illnesses. He completed some courses at first, second, and third year level, with distinction and high distinction. Alfredo also studied piano and was able to gain the 8th year piano grade.

Today, Alfredo is the full-time caregiver for his wife, who suffers from a number of disabilities. He also regularly raises funds for his local hospital, Gosford Hospital, by organizing fundraiser nights where he plays with other musicians. So far, he has helped to raise thousands of dollars. The money goes toward the needs of the hospital's patients with mental disorders. Alfredo also writes an online journal, *The Anti Stigma Crusaders*, which he uploads regularly at two or three month intervals.

Alfredo also provides support for online sufferers and uses his art to help people. While he is not a qualified music therapist, he does use music and art to help people online. Some mental health professionals often consult him for his lived experience and knowledge of psychology and music. He has written three books, including this one, two published and one that is free online. He also contributes by giving talks in universities about his experience with bipolar disorder.

Bibliograpy

Alvin, J., (1966.) *Music Therapy.* W. & J. Mackay & Co Ltd, Chatham, Kent.

Arieti, S., (1955) *Creativity: the magic synthesis.* Basic Books, United States of America.

Barber, B, (2008) *Draw everything.* Arcturus Publishing Limited, London.

Bath, H. (December 07, 2008). The Three Pillars of Trauma-Informed Care. *Reclaiming Children and Youth, 17,* 3, 17-21.

Cain, T. (2009, May). Addressing Trauma: The First Step in My Journey to Recovery. Retrieved September 5, 2016, from http://www.crisisprevention.com/CPI/media/Media/Blogs/addressing-trauma-the-first-step-in-my-journey-to-recovery.pdf

Capra, F. (1988). *Uncommon wisdom: Conversations with remarkable people.* New York: Simon and Schuster..

Carter, R., & Frith, C. D. (1998). *Mapping the mind.* Berkeley, CA: University of California Press..

Carson, S., (2010). *Your Creative Brain.* Published by Jossey-Bass and Wiley imprint, San Francisco.

Cirry, M., & Tubridy, A, (2001). *Going mad? Understanding mental illness.* Newleaf (An imprint of Gill & Macmillian Ltd), Doublin.

Churchland, P, M. (1993) *Matter and consciousness: a complementary introduction to the philosophy of mind.* MIT press, Cambridge, Massachusetts, London, England.

Curtis, C., Sensei. (2009, March 01). 2009 Shugyo Tassei Kigan Shiki Seminar. Retrieved September 05, 2016, from http://curtissensei.com/wp-content/uploads/2009/03/stks-seminar-ki-breathing-ki-meditation.pdf Linked from post http://curtissensei.com/?p=351

Doidge, N. (2007). *The brain that changes itself: Stories of personal triumph from the frontiers of brain science.* New York: Viking.

Gammell, R. H. I., & Degas, E. (1961). The shop-talk of Edgar Degas. Boston: University Press.

Goulston, M., & Goldberg, P. (1996). *Get out of your own way: Overcoming self-defeating behavior.* New York, NY: Berkley Pub. Group.

Holden, W., Kwan, N., Quine, R., Stark, R., Patrick, J., Mason, R., Osborn, P., ... Paramount Pictures Corporation. (1989). The World of Suzie Wong. Hollywood, CA: Paramount Pictures.

Holmes, J (1993) *Between art and science: Essays in psychotherapy and psychiatry,* Tavistock/Routledge, London and New York.

Kidman, A. (1999.) *Feeling Better: a guide to mood management.* Second Edition. Biochemical and General Services, Sydney.

Laycraft, K,. C. (2015). *The courage to create.* Aware Now Publishing, Canada.

Mason, R. (1957). The world of Suzie Wong. Cleveland: World Pub. Co.

Nilsson, B. J. (2010, March 20). Imagination Is More Important Than Knowledge Comments. Retrieved September 05, 2016, from http://www.saturdayeveningpost.com/2010/03/20/history/post-perspective/imagination-important-knowledge.html

Pahl, R. H. (2002). *Breaking away from the textbook: Creative ways to teach world history.* Vol. 2, the Enlightenment through the 20th century. Lanham, Md: Scarecrow.

Rettmann, D. R. (2009, March 1). Journal of Safe Management of Disruptive and Assaultive Behavior, 17(1). Retrieved September 5, 2016.

Shea, P. (n.d.). The Role of National Association of State Mental Health Programs Directors in Promoting Trauma-Informed Mental Health Care. Retrieved September 5, 2016, from www.nasmhpd.org

Shute, C. (October 01, 1968). The Comparative Phenomenology of Japanese Painting and Zen Buddhism. *Philosophy East and West, 18,* 4, 285-298.

Simonton, D. K., (1999) *Origins on genius: Darwinian perspective on creativity.* New York. Oxford University Press.

Smith, T.C. (1963-64). Incubation. In M.A. Runco and S.R. Pritzker (Eds.), *Encyclopedia of creativity* (vol. 2, pp. 39 – 43).

Starchenko, M. G., Bechtereva, N. P., Pakhomov, S. V., & Medvedev, S. V. (2003). Study of the brain organization of creative thinking. *Human Psychology, 29,*151=152.

Steele, W. and Raider, M. (2001). Clinician or witness: the intervener's relationship with traumatized children. *Reclaiming children and youth, 17* (3), 44–47.

Warburton, N. (2003.) *The art question.* Routledge, London.

Woolfolk, R. L., Parrish, M. W., & Murphy, S. M. (1985). The effective and negative imagery on motor skill performance. *Cognitive and research, 9,* 335-341.

World Health Organization. (2001). Mental Health: New understandings of hope. Geneva: World Health Organization.

Zotti, A. (2014.) *Alfredo's journey: An Artist's creative life with bipolar disorder.* Modern History Press, Ann Arbor.

Index

A

Adele, 119
Alzheimer's, 8, 148
Arc Riders, 115–16
Asperger's, 116, 117

B

bipolar, 39, 67, 150, 151
Bits and Pieces, 49–51
Boat People, The, 46–48
Bradley, D., 89–101
  bio, 148
Bradley, M.
  bio, 148
Bush, The, 17–19
butterfly effect, 106

C

calligraphy, 65–71
Carol's Story, 5–10
Chaos Theory, 76
charcoals, 89
choir, 111, 137, 149
collages, 78, 79, 81
Colours of Emotions, 41–43
creativity, 81
Creeper, The, 96–97

D

Dąbrowski, 79
Degas, 117, 130, 153
Dempsey, E.
  bio, 149
depression, 5, 6, 39, 64, 101,
  103, 104, 105, 106, 115, 119,
  129, 148, 149
Depression Trap, The, 38–41
DNA, 21, 24, 25

E

Eliot, T.S., 50
escapism, 135
extrinsic values, 73

F

Franklin, R., 21, 24

G

Gosford Hospital, 113, 115, 151
Guernica, 33
Gum trees, 19

H

hexagrams, 78
hip hop, 119, 123, 148
Holden, W., 117
homeless, 113, 115, 117, 120,
  128, 129, 150
Houdini, 135, 136

I

I Ching, 78
If Only I Could Paint, 133
individuation, 77

J

Japan, 65–66
Jordan, M., 121

K

Kariong, 5–10
  defined, 6
  Grandmother, 12, 13
Kidman, N., 24
Krabbendam, J., 76

L

Lautrec, T., 114
Laycraft, C.
  bio, 143–44
Let Me Touch You There, 134
Lopizzo, M., 109–11
Luciano Zotti, 14–16

M

Mann, S., i
  bio, 142

Marley, R., 119, 127
Marx, 106
Maslow, A., 79
music, 111, 137

N

Nilsson, B., 118

O

Oriental Dream, 26–28

P

Painting
  eyes closed, 65–71
Pearson, C., i, 131, 139–40
Pena, A., 133, 134
  bio, 149
Photograph 51, 20–22, 24
Piaget, 79
Piano Player, The, 44–45
Picasso, 33, 36, 118, 125
Plato, 111
Polish artists, 79
Positive Disintegration, 79
POTCar, 131, 140, 142
PTSD, 63, 64, 115

R

Rich, R., 63–64
  bio, 145–46
Rogers, C., 79
Rosalind's Eyes, 23–25

S

Scerri, V.P., 65–71
  bio, 147
schizophrenia, 118
September 11, 32–34
Serbia, 5
sexual abuse, 89, 93, 94
Shore, The, 58–59
singing, 137
Sydee, C., 115–16
systemic value dimension, 73

T

Tyler, B., 119

U

Uncle Sam, 29–31

V

Van Gogh, 47, 114
Venice, 55–57

Violin on a Rock, 35–37, 45

W

Wilber, K., 81
Witkacy, 82
Wright, J.
  bio, 149

X

X-Ray, 24

Y

Yesterday, Today, and
  Tomorrow, the Flowers, 52–
  54
Yugoslavia, 5, 7

Z

Zotti, A.
  bio, 150–51

More than a just a journey, Alfredo gives us a blueprint for humane treatment of mental illness

In 1981, twenty-three-year old Alfredo Zotti began his lifelong challenge of living with Bipolar II Disorder. He quickly hit rock bottom, spending time as a homeless person and turning to street drugs and alcohol to medicate his symptoms. After hospitalization and careful outpatient monitoring, he became a successful musician and completed university. In 2004, he started to mentor sufferers of mental illness, and together, they developed an online journal. Alfredo now sees mental illness from a new perspective, not of disadvantages but advantages. In his words: "Having a mental illness can be a blessing if we work on ourselves."

In this memoir and critique of mental illness, the reader will learn:

- How empathic listening and being with someone can help calm that person's symptoms
- The power of singing to create a safe space in a community
- Why spirituality can be a key component in the healing process
- The connections between mental illness, artistic expression, and people who think differently
- The impact of childhood trauma on our psyche and its role in mental illness
- The dangers of antipsychotics and antidepressants
- The amazing connection between heart and brain and how we can cultivate it
- The challenges of love and marriage between partners with Bipolar Disorder

Original music composed and recorded by the author is available for download by readers.

"Alfredo's story and his insights into the causes and treatment of mental ill-health are incredibly moving and impressive. His humanity, intelligence, creativity and his generosity and compassion towards people affected by mental illness and dedicated mental health professionals shine through the pages of his book."

-- Professor Patrick McGorry, AO MD PhD,
Executive Director, OYH Research Centre, University of Melbourne

"As a clinician and academic, one can study and research ever known aspect of a disorder and write scholarly articles for learned journals, but none of this holds the potency of an individual relaying his or her lived experience. Alfredo does just this in his inimitable style, offering hope at every juncture to those who travel a similar road. The story should be read by clinicians, academics and sufferers alike."

--Professor Trevor Waring AM, Clinical Psychologist,
Con-Joint Professor of Psychology, University of Newcastle

Learn more at www.AlfredoZotti.com
From the World Voices Series at Modern History Press
www.ModernHistoryPress.com